PRENTICE HALL LITERATURE

PENGUIN EDITION

Skills Development Workbook

Grade Nine

PEARSON
Prentice Hall

Upper Saddle River, New Jersey
Boston, Massachusetts

Pearson Prentice Hall™ is a trademark of Pearson Education, Inc.
Pearson® is a registered trademark of Pearson plc.
Prentice Hall® is a registered trademark of Pearson Education, Inc.

ISBN 0-13-165384-9

2 3 4 5 6 7 8 9 10   10 09 08 07 06

Contents

Unit 1 Fiction and Nonfiction

Part 1 Make Predictions

Part 2 Author's Purpose

UNIT 2 Short Stories

Part 1 Make Inferences

Part 2 Cause and Effect

UNIT 3 Types of Nonfiction

Part 1 Main Idea and Supporting Details

Part 2 Analyze Persuasive Texts

UNIT 4 Poetry

Part 1 Read Fluently

"Uncoiling" by Pat Mora

Poetry Collection: Langston Hughes; William Wordsworth; Gabriela Mistral; Jean de Sponde

Poetry Collection: Richard Brautigan; Emily Dickinson; Stanley Kunitz

Poetry Collection: Walter Dean Myers; Alfred, Lord Tennyson; May Swenson

Poetry Collection: Yusef Komunyakaa; Lewis Carroll; Edgar Allan Poe

Poetry by Mary Tall Mountain; Galway Kinnell; Naomi Shihab Nye

Part 2 Paraphrase

UNIT 5 Drama

Part 1 Summarize

Part 2 Draw Conclusions

UNIT 6 Themes in Literature

Part 1 Cultural and Historical Context

Part 2 Compare and Contrast

"Three Skeleton Key" by George Toudouze

"The Red-headed League" by Sir Arthur Conan Doyle

"There Is a Longing" by Chief Dan George

"Glory and Hope" by Nelson Mandela

"Pecos Bill: The Cyclone" by Harold W. Felton

"Perseus" by Edith Hamilton

Name _____   Date _____

Elizabeth McCracken
Listening and Viewing

Segment 1: Meet Elizabeth McCracken
- Where does Elizabeth McCracken get inspiration for the characters she writes about in her books?
- If you were writing a fictional story, would you base your characters on real people or invent them entirely? Why?

_____

_____

_____

Segment 2: Fiction and Nonfiction
- Why does Elizabeth McCracken enjoy writing fiction?
- Why do you think it is important for a fiction writer to also read nonfiction books?

_____

_____

_____

Segment 3: The Writing Process
- Why is it important for Elizabeth McCracken to develop her characters?
- Which fictional character left a lasting impression on you? Explain.

_____

_____

_____

Segment 4: The Rewards of Writing
- What advice does Elizabeth McCracken offer young writers?
- What do you "get out" of reading fiction?

_____

_____

_____

Learning About Fiction and Nonfiction

The following chart compares and contrasts two types of prose literature.

Characteristics	Fiction	Nonfiction
Elements	Fiction tells about **characters,** *imaginary* people or animals. They participate in a **plot,** or a series of made-up events, that contains a **conflict,** or problem, to be solved. The plot takes place in one or more **settings.** The story conveys a **theme,** or idea about life.	Nonfiction tells about *real* people, animals, places, things, experiences, and ideas. Nonfiction can contain facts, opinions, and ideas.
Sample forms	short stories, novels, novellas	articles, autobiographies, biographies, essays, journals
Author's purpose	to entertain	to explain, inform, persuade, or entertain

A. DIRECTIONS: *Write* fiction *or* nonfiction *to identify the kind of literature described.*

_____ 1. a piece of literature that features a talking tiger

_____ 2. a piece of literature about travel to Japan

_____ 3. a piece of literature about the lessons two friends learn about themselves when they go to summer camp

_____ 4. a piece of literature that explains how a runner trains for victory

B. DIRECTIONS: *Read the paragraph. Then, answer the questions that follow.*

   The modem on Alicia's laptop computer had been blown apart in the lightning storm. Try as she would, she could not connect to the phone line. But Alicia refused to give up. Opening the cover on her cell phone, she held the instrument firmly and pressed a silver-colored button for precisely three seconds. Within another three seconds, she was small enough to slither through the back of the laptop. She saw the modem glinting on the motherboard. She was ready to begin the repair job.

1. Does the preceding paragraph introduce a piece of fiction or nonfiction? _____

2. Explain your answer to Question 1.

_____

_____

Name _____ Date _____

from **The Giant's House** by Elizabeth McCracken
Model Selection: Fiction

A fictional story is told by a **narrator.** The narrator may or may not be a character in the story. If the narrator is part of the story, he or she tells the plot using **first-person point of view,** with pronouns such as *I, me,* and *our.* If the narrator stands outside the story, he or she tells it in **third-person point of view,** using such pronouns as *he, she,* and *them.*

In reading fiction, you need to distinguish between **plot** and **theme.** The plot is what happens. The theme is the message carried by the plot, the characters, and the setting.

A. DIRECTIONS: *The excerpt from* The Giant's House *is a piece of fiction. Answer these questions about the narrator of* The Giant's House.

1. Is the narrator of *The Giant's House* inside or outside the story? _____

2. Does the narrator use first-person or third-person point of view? _____

B. DIRECTIONS: *Study the following example, which distinguishes between the plot of a story and its theme. Then, in your own words, state the plot of* A Giant's House *and the theme that grows out of the plot.*

Plot of story:	Maria practices her lines for the school play every day. She wants to bring her character to life, so she experiments in front of a mirror with different gestures, facial expressions, and tones of voice. On opening night, she turns in a first-rate performance, and the audience applauds warmly.
Theme of story:	Hard work leads to success.

Plot of excerpt from *The Giant's House:*

_____

_____

_____

Theme of excerpt from *The Giant's House:*

_____

_____

_____

Name _____ Date _____

"**Desiderata**" by Elizabeth McCracken
Model Selection: Nonfiction

The author of a piece of nonfiction has one or more purposes for writing. The purpose or purposes relate to the kind of nonfiction the author is producing.

- The purpose of **narrative** nonfiction is to tell about a real-life event. Examples of narrative nonfiction include autobiographies and memoirs. Some narrative nonfiction is **reflective writing,** which gives the writer's thoughts and feelings about a personal experience, an idea, or a concern. Examples of reflective writing include reflective essays and journals.
- The purpose of **expository** nonfiction is to inform or to explain. Examples of this type of nonfiction include analytical essays and research reports.
- The purpose of **persuasive** nonfiction is to make the reader act or think in a certain way. Examples include editorials and political speeches.
- The purpose of **descriptive** nonfiction is to create mental images for the reader. Examples include character sketches and scientific observations.

DIRECTIONS: *Authors often have more than one purpose in mind when they write a piece of nonfiction. Here is a list of purposes:*

to explain	to inform	to report a real-life event
to persuade	to entertain	to share thoughts and experiences

What two purposes do you think Elizabeth McCracken might have had in mind when she wrote "Desiderata"? Support your answer with reasons and examples from the selection.

_____

_____

_____

_____

_____

_____

_____

_____

_____

_____

_____

_____

_____

_____

Name _____ Date _____

"The Washwoman" by Isaac Bashevis Singer
Literary Analysis: Narrative Essay

A **narrative essay** is a short piece of nonfiction in which the author tells a story about a real person or event. In a narrative essay, the author chooses to include **significant details** that help move the story forward or that help to make his or her point about the subject. For example, if Singer were writing a narrative essay about his own childhood, he would include the significant detail that his father was a Hasidic rabbi who presided over a rabbinic court. In the same essay about his childhood, however, he would not mention the fact that Anjelica Huston starred in the 1989 movie *Enemies, a Love Story*, which is based on one of Singer's novels. That would not be a significant detail for an essay about his childhood. As you read, notice how the author's choice of significant details influences your impressions of the people and events he or she describes.

DIRECTIONS: *Follow the directions to answer each numbered item.*

1. In no more than two or three sentences, summarize the essay's narrative, or story.

    _____

    _____

2. Now, look back over the essay. Find two significant details that Singer includes about (a) the washwoman's appearance, (b) what she says, and (c) what she does. Write the details exactly as Singer expresses them, enclosing the words and phrases in quotation marks.

    (a) Her appearance _____

    _____

    _____

    (b) What she says _____

    _____

    (c) What she does _____

    _____

    _____

    ---

3. Think about why Singer wrote this essay. What main point about the washwoman do you think he makes in this essay?

    _____

    _____

    _____

Name _____ Date _____

"The Washwoman" by Isaac Bashevis Singer
Reading: Ask Questions to Make Predictions

A **prediction** is an informed guess about what will happen later in a narrative. Predictions are based on details in the text and on your own experience. When **making and verifying predictions,** predict what will happen, and then read on to see if the prediction is correct.

- One way to make predictions is to pause periodically while reading and **ask questions** about text details and events. You can ask yourself questions such as *Why does the author mention this detail? How might it become important later on?* Then, look for the answers to those questions as you read ahead.
- As you read, use the following chart to record your predictions. Then, see how many of your predictions were correct.

DIRECTIONS: *In the left column are some of the major events in "The Washwoman." As you read, ask yourself questions about what may be the outcome or consequence of each event. Write your questions in the center column. In the right column, record your predictions. The first one has been done for you.*

Event	Question	Prediction
1. The frail old washwoman works hard to produce beautiful, clean laundry.	Will the Singer family be satisfied with her work?	The Singers will like her work and employ her for many years.
2. She has a rich son who does not see her or give her any money.		
3. The rich son gets married but does not invite her to the wedding.		
4. One very cold winter day, the washwoman staggers away under a huge bundle of laundry.		
5. Weeks pass, and she does not return.		

Name _____ Date _____

"The Washwoman" by Isaac Bashevis Singer
Vocabulary Builder

Word List

> forebears   rancor   atonement   obstinacy

A. DIRECTIONS: *For each item below, think about the meaning of the underlined word, and then answer the question.*

1. You are the judge in a case in which two adults have been found guilty of being cruel to their pet dogs. What do you think is an appropriate <u>atonement</u>?

   _____

   _____

2. Explain the difference between *anger* and <u>rancor</u>.

   _____

   _____

3. Describe something that a person might have from his or her <u>forebears</u>.

   _____

   _____

4. You are part of a small group assigned to work on a project that is due in a week. What would you say to someone whose <u>obstinacy</u> is preventing the group from getting started?

   _____

   _____

B. DIRECTIONS: *Follow the instructions to use each vocabulary word in a sentence.*

1. Use <u>rancor</u> in a sentence about unsportsmanlike conduct.

   _____

2. Use <u>obstinacy</u> in a sentence about a two-year-old.

   _____

3. Write a sentence about respecting something a king inherited from his <u>forebears</u>.

   _____

4. Use <u>atonement</u> in a sentence about littering a public park.

   _____

"The Washwoman" by Isaac Bashevis Singer

Support for Writing an Anecdote

Use the following cluster diagram to gather information for your **anecdote**—your very brief story about a person whom you admire. In the middle circle, write the name of a person whom you admire. In the surrounding circles, write several characteristics that you like and respect about that person. (You do not have to fill in all of the circles.) Then, jot down some notes about a specific event that shows what the person is like.

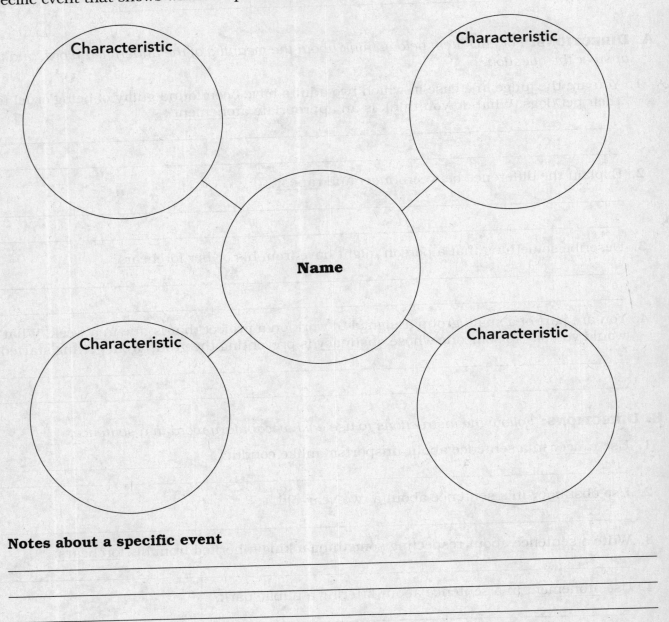

Notes about a specific event

_____

_____

_____

Now, write your anecdote. Describe in detail a specific event or action that illustrates what you admire about the person whom you have chosen. Be sure to tell what you learned from the person's actions.

Name _____ Date _____

"New Directions" by Maya Angelou
Literary Analysis: Narrative Essay

A **narrative essay** is a short piece of nonfiction in which the author tells a story about a real person or event. In a narrative essay, the author chooses to include **significant details** that help move the story forward or that help to make his or her point about the subject. For example, if Maya Angelou were writing a narrative essay about her own childhood, she would include the significant detail that she and her brother Bailey spent much of their childhood living with their grandmother in Stamps, Arkansas. In such an essay about her childhood, however, she would not mention the fact that in 1993, at President Clinton's inauguration, she recited her poem "On the Pulse of Morning." That would not be a significant detail for an essay about her childhood. As you read, notice how the author's choice of significant details influences your impressions of the people and events he or she describes.

DIRECTIONS: *Follow the directions to answer each numbered item.*

1. In no more than two or three sentences, summarize the story that the author tells in the essay.

   _____

   _____

   _____

2. Now, look back over the essay. Find two significant details that Angelou includes about (a) Annie Johnson's appearance, (b) what she says, and (c) what she does. Write the details exactly as Angelou expresses them, enclosing the words and phrases in quotation marks.

(a) Annie Johnson's appearance _____

_____

_____

(b) What she says _____

_____

_____

(c) What she does _____

_____

_____

---

3. Think about why Maya Angelou wrote this essay. What points or main ideas do you think she makes in this essay? _____

   _____

   _____

   _____

Name _____ Date _____

"**New Directions**" by Maya Angelou

Reading: Ask Questions to Make Predictions

A **prediction** is an informed guess about what will happen later in a narrative. Predictions are based on details in the text and on your own experience. When **making and verifying predictions,** predict what will happen, and then read on to see if the prediction is correct.

- One way to make predictions is to pause periodically while reading and **ask questions** about text details and events. You can ask yourself questions such as *Why does the author mention this detail? How might it become important later on?* Then, look for the answers to those questions as you read ahead.
- As you read, use the following chart to record your questions and the predictions you make from them. Then, see if your predictions were correct.

DIRECTIONS: *In the left column are some of the major events in "New Directions." As you read, consider what you think may be the outcome or consequence of each event. Write your questions in the center column. In the right column, record your predictions.*

Event	Question	Prediction
1. Annie Johnson's marriage ends, leaving her with two young sons.		
2. She needs to earn money to support herself and her family.		
3. She starts to sell her home-made meat pies to workers at the lumber mill and cotton gin.		
4. She is so successful selling pies that she builds a stall between the cotton gin and lumber mill.		

Name _____ Date _____

"New Directions" by Maya Angelou
Vocabulary Builder

Word List

| amicably | meticulously | ominous | unpalatable |

A. DIRECTIONS: *For each of the following items, think about the meaning of the italicized word, and then answer the question.*

1. What happens when two people settle an argument *amicably?*

   _____

   _____

2. If you were to clean a kitchen *meticulously*, what would it look like when you finish?

   _____

   _____

3. What kind of weather would you describe as *ominous?*

   _____

   _____

4. What task do you find most *unpalatable?*

   _____

   _____

B. DIRECTIONS: *Each item consists of a related pair of words in CAPITAL LETTERS followed by four other pairs of words. Choose the pair that best expresses a relationship similar to that expressed in the pair in capital letters. Circle the letter of your choice.*

1. METICULOUSLY : CARELESSLY ::
   A. aged : elderly
   B. community : neighborhood
   C. immediately : finally
   D. substitute : change

2. DISTASTEFUL : UNPALATABLE ::
   A. pleasant : unpleasant
   B. studious : excellent
   C. barbaric : civilized
   D. frank : forthright

3. OMINOUS : WARNING ::
   A. curious : question
   B. powerful : weak
   C. chaos : confusion
   D. hopeful : pessimistic

Name _____ Date _____

"**New Directions**" by Maya Angelou
Support for Writing an Anecdote

Use the following cluster diagram to gather information for your **anecdote**—your very brief story. In the middle circle, write the name of a person whom you admire. In the surrounding circles, write several characteristics that you like and respect about that person. (You do not have to fill in all of the circles.) Then, make some notes about a specific event that shows what the person is like.

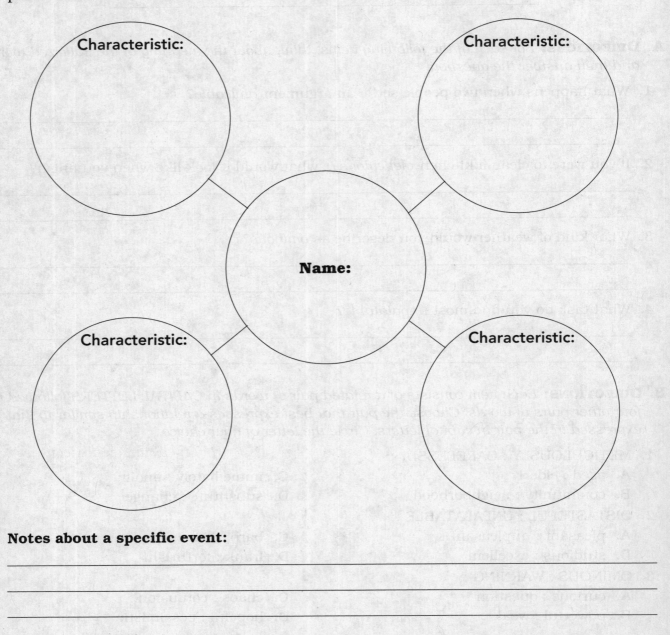

Notes about a specific event:

_____

_____

_____

_____

Now, write your anecdote. Describe in detail a specific event or action that illustrates what you admire about the person whom you have chosen. Be sure to tell what you learned from the person's actions.

Name _____ Date _____

"The Washwoman" by Isaac Bashevis Singer
"New Directions" by Maya Angelou

Build Language Skills: Vocabulary

The Latin Roots -part- and -volve-

When you *participate* in an activity, you *involve* yourself in it. Both *participate* and *involve* have Latin roots. *Participate* has the Latin root -part-, meaning "portion or part of." To *participate* is to "take part." *Involve* has the Latin root -volve-, meaning "roll." Involve means "roll in," or "include." The root -volve- is closely related to the root -volut-, which also means "roll."

A. DIRECTIONS: *Use a dictionary to look up the meaning of each of the following words containing the root -part- or -volv-. Write one of the meanings for each word. Then, write a sentence using the word in a context that makes its meaning clear.*

1. **partial** Meaning: _____

   Sentence: _____

2. **particle** Meaning: _____

   Sentence: _____

3. **evolve** Meaning: _____

   Sentence: _____

4. **revolution** Meaning: _____

   Sentence: _____

5. **volume** Meaning: _____

   Sentence: _____

Academic Vocabulary Practice

B. DIRECTIONS: *Answer each question by writing a complete sentence in which you use the italicized Academic Vocabulary word.*

1. Would you prefer reading a *contemporary* story or one written by a nineteenth-century author? Explain.

   _____

2. Name one literary element that *contributes* to a story's success. Explain why it is important.

   _____

3. Explain how a quiet story, such as "The Washwoman," manages to *involve* the reader although nothing exciting happens in the story.

   _____

4. How does predicting outcomes help the reader *participate* actively in the reading process?

   _____

5. Identify the *specific* setting (the time and place) for Maya Angelou's story "New Directions."

   _____

"The Washwoman" by Isaac Bashevis Singer
"New Directions" by Maya Angelou
Build Language Skills: Grammar

Common and Proper Nouns

A **noun** is a word that names a person, place, or thing. Nouns name things that can be seen and touched as well as those that cannot be seen and touched. Notice in the following chart that among the things nouns can name are ideas, actions, conditions, and qualities.

People:	Aunt Cele, Esteban, musicians, doctor
Places:	Sacramento, Lincoln Park Zoo, mountain, desert, park, lake
See and touch:	grass, dish, table, truck
Ideas and actions:	freedom, confusion, election, censorship
Conditions and qualities:	optimism, courage, shyness, bewilderment

A **common noun** names any one of a class of people, places, or things—for example, *day*, *river*, or *woman*. A **proper noun** names a specific person, place, or thing and always begins with a capital letter—for example, *Tuesday*, *Cuyahoga River*, or *Harriet Tubman*.

In the following example, the common nouns are underlined and the proper nouns are in boldface.

Example from "New Directions"

He did not tell her that he knew a minister in **Enid** with whom he could study and who had a friendly, unmarried daughter. They parted amicably, **Annie** keeping the one-room house and William taking most of the cash to carry him to Oklahoma.

A. DIRECTIONS: *In each numbered item, underline the common nouns and draw a circle around the proper nouns.*

1. The only Gentile in the building was the janitor. Fridays he would come for a tip, his Friday money.
2. She lived on Krochmalna Street too, but at the other end, near the Wola section.
3. My mother spoke a little Polish, and the old woman would talk with her about many things.
4. The son had not invited the old mother to his wedding, but she went to the church and waited at the steps to see her son lead the "young lady" to the altar.

B. DIRECTIONS: *Write a three-sentence paragraph in which you describe the town where you live. Use at least three common nouns and three proper nouns in your paragraph. Remember that proper nouns are always capitalized.*

_____

_____

_____

_____

Name _____ Date _____

"Sonata for Harp and Bicycle" by Joan Aiken
Literary Analysis: Plot, Foreshadowing, and Suspense

Plot is the sequence of events in a narrative. It is structured around a **conflict,** or problem, and it can be divided into the following parts:

- **Rising action**—the central conflict is introduced
- **Climax**—the high point of intensity in the conflict
- **Falling action**—the conflict's intensity lessens
- **Resolution**—the conflict concludes and loose ends are tied up

Writers use a variety of techniques to keep readers interested in the plot. One of these, **foreshadowing,** is the use of clues to hint at events that will happen later in a story. Authors use this technique to create **suspense,** a feeling of tension that keeps readers wondering what will happen next.

Read the following passage from "Sonata for Harp and Bicycle" in which Jason Ashgrove has a conversation with his secretary, Miss Golden. They are working on advertising copy for a cereal called Oat Crisps:

> "What do you want for your birthday, Miss Golden? Sherry? Fudge? Bubble bath?"

> "I want to go away with a clear conscience about Oat Crisps," Miss Golden retorted. It was not true; what she chiefly wanted was Mr. Jason Ashgrove, but he had not realized this yet.

What possibility does the passage foreshadow? Do you think the story will make clear whether or not Miss Golden and Mr. Ashgrove have a romance?

A. DIRECTIONS: *Read the following passage, and identify details the author uses to create suspense. Underline the words in the passage that make you curious about the outcome.*

> Jason was frustrated. "You'll be sorry," he said. "I shall do something desperate."

> "Oh, no, you mustn't!" Her eyes were large with fright. She ran from the room and was back within a couple of moments, still drying her hands.

> "If I took you out for a coffee, couldn't you give me just a tiny hint?"

> Side by side Miss Golden and Mr. Ashgrove ran along the green-floored passages, battled down the white marble stairs among the hundred other employees from the tenth floor, the nine hundred from the floors below.

B. DIRECTIONS: *Identify two clues the author gives that foreshadow the story's ending. Did you expect the story's ending, or were you surprised? Describe your response and tell why you reacted that way.*

Clue 1: _____

Clue 2: _____

My response to story's ending: _____
_____

"Sonata for Harp and Bicycle" by Joan Aiken
Reading: Read Ahead to Verify Predictions

A **prediction** is an informed guess about what will happen later in a narrative. **Making and verifying predictions** keeps you actively involved in the story you are reading.

- Notice details that may foreshadow future events. Make predictions based on those details, and then read on to verify your predictions. If a prediction turns out to be wrong, evaluate your reasoning to determine whether you misread details or whether the author purposely created false expectations in order to surprise you later in the story.
- Use a chart like the one shown to record your predictions and evaluate their accuracy. Analyze any inaccurate predictions to determine why they were incorrect.

The key to making accurate predictions is paying close attention to the story you read. In "Sonata for Harp and Bicycle," the author provides many colorful details about what will happen.

Aiken's Original: Jason turned and stared at Grimes Buildings. Somewhere, he knew, there was a back way in, a service entrance.

Prediction: Jason is going to enter the Grimes Buildings through the back way.

DIRECTIONS: *Fill in the second and third columns of the following chart. Write your predictions based on the details in the first column. Then, read ahead to find out the outcome of your predictions, and record the outcomes.*

Details	My Prediction	Outcome
1. The bell stopped beside him, and then there was a moment when his heart tried to shake itself loose in his chest. He was looking into two eyes carved out of expressionless air; he was held by two hands knotted together out of the width of the dark.		
2. "We must remedy the matter, Berenice. We must not begrudge our new-found happiness to others."		
3. "We don't want our evening to be spoiled by the thought of a curse hanging over us, he said, so this is the practical thing to do. Hang onto the roses."		

Name _____ Date _____

Word List

tantalizingly	furtive	reciprocate

A. DIRECTIONS: *In each of the following items, think about the meaning of the italicized Word List word, and then answer the question.*

1. You have forgotten your key, the house is locked, and no one is at home. Describe your *furtive* attempt to enter your house.

   _____

   _____

2. "Look what I've got!" Dina *tantalizingly* waves two tickets to tonight's sold-out concert in front of your face. What do you think she plans to do with the tickets?

   _____

   _____

3. Kezia and her mother have invited you to join them for Thanksgiving dinner. Think of two ways in which you could *reciprocate*.

   _____

   _____

B. DIRECTIONS: *Follow the instructions to write sentences using the vocabulary words.*

1. Use *tantalizingly* in a sentence about a favorite food.
2. Use *furtive* in a sentence about a cat.
3. Use *reciprocate* in a sentence about doing a favor for someone.

C. DIRECTIONS: *Write the letter of the word that is the best synonym for the numbered word.*

____ 1. furtive
   - A. quiet
   - B. stolen
   - C. sneaky
   - D. honest

____ 2. reciprocate
   - A. refuse
   - B. return
   - C. respond
   - D. renew

____ 3. tantalizingly
   - A. with great care
   - B. with a lot of noise
   - C. in an angry way
   - D. in a teasing way

17

Name _____ Date _____

"Sonata for Harp and Bicycle" by Joan Aiken
Support for Writing a Critique

Use the following chart to list the qualities that make the ending of a story either satisfactory or unsatisfactory. Then, put a check mark in front of the qualities that you think apply to "Sonata for Harp and Bicycle."

A Satisfactory Ending	An Unsatisfactory Ending
❑ _____	❑ _____
❑ _____	❑ _____
❑ _____	❑ _____
❑ _____	❑ _____
❑ _____	❑ _____
❑ _____	❑ _____

Now, use your notes to write your critique in which you evaluate the ending of "Sonata for Harp and Bicycle."

"The Cask of Amontillado" by Edgar Allan Poe
Literary Analysis: Plot, Foreshadowing, and Suspense

Plot is the sequence of events in a narrative. It is structured around a **conflict,** or problem, and it can be divided into the following parts:

- **Rising action**—the central conflict is introduced
- **Climax**—the high point of intensity in the conflict
- **Falling action**—the conflict's intensity lessens
- **Resolution**—the conflict concludes and loose ends are tied up

Writers use a variety of techniques to keep readers interested in the plot. One of these, **foreshadowing,** is the use of clues to hint at events that will happen later in a story. Authors use this technique to create **suspense,** a feeling of tension that keeps readers wondering what will happen next.

Read the following passage, which is the opening paragraph of "The Cask of Amontillado."

> The thousand injuries of Fortunato I had borne as I best could, but when he ventured upon insult I vowed revenge. You, who so well know the nature of my soul, will not suppose, however, that I gave utterance to a threat. At *length* I would be avenged; this was a point definitely settled—but the very definitiveness with which it was resolved precluded the idea of risk. I must not only punish but punish with impunity.

In the opening paragraph, what details does Poe include that suggest something about the narrator's personality and his plans? The paragraph arouses our curiosity: What does the narrator plan to do, and how can he possibly get away without being punished?

A. DIRECTIONS: *Read the following passage, and watch for details the author uses to create suspense. Underline the words and phrases in the passage that make you curious about the outcome.*

> The wine sparkled in his eyes and the bells jingled. My own fancy grew warm with the Medoc. We had passed through long walls of piled skeletons, with casks and puncheons intermingling, into the inmost recesses of the catacombs. I paused again, and this time I made bold to seize Fortunato by an arm above the elbow.
>
> "The niter!" I said; "see, it increases. It hangs like moss upon the vaults. We are below the river's bed. The drops of moisture trickle among the bones. Come, we will go back ere it is too late. Your cough—"
>
> "It is nothing," he said; "let us go on. But first, another draft of the Medoc."

B. DIRECTIONS: *Identify two clues the author gives that foreshadow the story's ending. Did you expect the story's ending, or were you surprised? Describe your response and tell why you reacted that way.*

Clue 1: _____

Clue 2: _____

My response to story's ending: _____

_____

"The Cask of Amontillado" by Edgar Allan Poe
Reading: Read Ahead to Make and Verify Predictions

A **prediction** is an informed guess about what will happen later in a narrative. **Making and verifying predictions** keeps you actively involved in the story you are reading.

- Notice details that may foreshadow future events. Make predictions based on those details, and then read on to verify your predictions. If a prediction turns out to be wrong, evaluate your reasoning to determine whether you misread details or whether the author purposely created false expectations in order to surprise you later in the story.
- Use a chart like the one shown to record your predictions and evaluate their accuracy. Analyze any inaccurate predictions to determine why they were incorrect.

The key to making accurate predictions is paying close attention to the story's details as you read. In "The Cask of Amontillado," the author provides many colorful details that serve as hints about what will happen.

Poe's original:	I took from their sconces two flambeaux, and giving one to Fortunato, bowed him through several suites of rooms to the archway that led to the vaults. I passed down a long and winding staircase, requesting him to be cautious as he followed. We came at length to the foot of the descent, and stood together upon the damp ground of the catacombs of the Montresors.
Prediction:	The narrator is going to do something terrible to Fortunato in the catacombs.

DIRECTIONS: *Fill in the columns on the following chart. In the second column, write your prediction based on the details in the first column. Then, read ahead to find out the outcome. How closely did your predictions match the outcomes? Record the outcomes in the third column.*

Details	My Prediction	Outcome
1. "Thus speaking, Fortunato possessed himself of my arm; and putting on a mask of black silk and drawing a *roquelaure* closely about my person, I suffered him to hurry me to my palazzo."		
2. "There were no attendants at home; they had absconded to make merry in honor of the time."		
3. It was in vain that Fortunato, uplifting his dull torch, endeavored to pry into the depth of the recess. Its termination the feeble light did not enable us to see. "Proceed," I said: "herein is the Amontillado. . . ."		

Name _____ Date _____

"The Cask of Amontillado" by Edgar Allan Poe
Vocabulary Builder

Word List

| precluded | retribution | explicit |

A. DIRECTIONS: *For each of the following items, think about the meaning of the italicized Word List word, and then answer the question.*

1. Give a new friend *explicit* directions on how to get from your homeroom to the gym.

   _____

   _____

   _____

   _____

2. Explain to your teacher what happened that *precluded* your turning in your research paper on the day it was due.

   _____

   _____

   _____

3. What do you think is an appropriate *retribution* for people who paint graffiti on subways and other public property?

   _____

   _____

   _____

B. DIRECTIONS: *Write the letter of the word that is most nearly* opposite *in meaning to the Word List word.*

____ 1. precluded

    A. allowed   B. prevented   C. discouraged   D. interrupted

____ 2. retribution

    A. punishment   B. reward   C. criticism   D. response

____ 3. explicit

    A. distinct   B. clear   C. complete   D. vague

"The Cask of Amontillado" by Edgar Allan Poe
Support for Writing a Critique

Use the following chart to think of all the qualities that make a story suspenseful. Then, put a check mark in front of the qualities that you think apply to "The Cask of Amontillado."

Qualities That Make a Story Suspenseful
❑ _____
_____
_____
❑ _____
_____
_____
❑ _____
_____
_____
_____
❑ _____
_____
_____
_____
❑ _____
_____
_____
_____
❑ _____
_____
_____
_____

Now, use your notes to write your critique in which you evaluate the suspense in "The Cask of Amontillado."

"**Sonata for Harp and Bicycle**" by Joan Aiken
"**The Cask of Amontillado**" by Edgar Allan Poe
Build Language Skills: Vocabulary

The Latin Root -*tempor*-

Several English words come from the Latin root -*tempor*-, which means "time." *Tempo*, which means "the rate of activity or pace," and *temporary*, which means "lasting for a limited time," can be traced back to this root.

A. DIRECTIONS: *Complete the following word maps for the words* contemporary *and* extemporaneous.

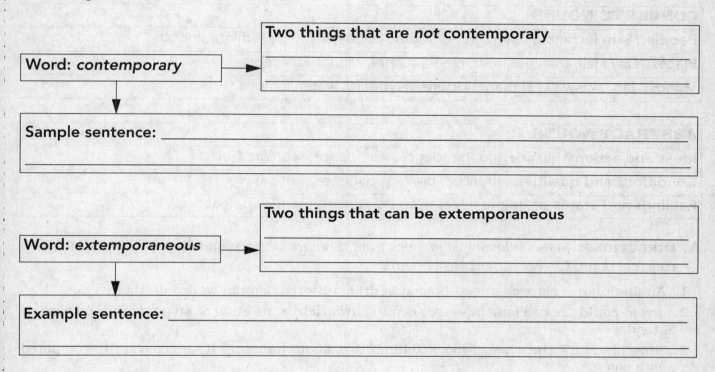

Academic Vocabulary Practice

B. DIRECTIONS: *For each of the following words, write a synonym in the space provided.*

1. contemporary: _____
2. contributes: _____
3. involve: _____
4. participate: _____
5. specific: _____

Name _____ Date _____

"Sonata for Harp and Bicycle" by Joan Aiken
"The Cask of Amontillado" by Edgar Allan Poe
Build Language Skills: Grammar

Abstract and Concrete Nouns

A **noun** is a word that names a person, place, or thing. Nouns name things that can be seen and touched as well as those that cannot be seen and touched. **Concrete nouns** refer to items that can be known by the senses—things that we can see, hear, taste, smell, or touch. **Abstract nouns** refer to ideas, qualities, states of being, and feelings—things that can be known only through the mind.

CONCRETE NOUNS
People: Sam Richman, sister, grandmother, Edgar Allan Poe, athlete, friend
Places: City Hall, Market Street, creek, school, Mount Rushmore
Things: raft, sidewalk, airplane, kittens, keyboard, water, lemons

ABSTRACT NOUNS
Ideas and actions: justice, independence, war, peace, reunion, trust
Conditions and qualities: strength, bravery, patience, optimism
Feelings and states of being: love, disappointment, friendship, fear

A. DIRECTIONS: *In the following sentences from "Sonata for Harp and Bicycle," underline every concrete noun. Circle every abstract noun.*

1. An ambulance clanged, a taxi hooted, a drill stuttered, a siren wailed on the river. . . .

2. Jason could see two long passages coming toward him, meeting at an acute angle where he stood.

3. "How about it?" the whisper mocked him. "How about jumping? It's an easy death compared with some."

4. "We must remedy the matter, Berenice. We must not begrudge our new-found happiness to others."

B. DIRECTIONS: *Write a paragraph in which you describe a person whom you know well. Use at least three concrete and three abstract nouns in your paragraph.*

_____

_____

_____

_____

_____

Name _____ Date _____

"Checkouts" by Cynthia Rylant
"The Girl Who Can" by Ama Ata Aidoo
Literary Analysis: Point of View

Point of view is the perspective from which a story is narrated, or told.

- **First-person point of view:** The narrator is a character who participates in the action of the story and uses the first-person pronouns *I* and *me.*
- **Third-person point of view:** The narrator is not a character in the story but is a voice out-side the action. The narrator uses the third-person pronouns *he, she, her, they,* and *them* to refer to all characters. There are two kinds of third-person points of view. In the **third-person omniscient** point of view, the narrator knows everything, including the thoughts and feelings of all the characters. In the **third-person limited** point of view, the narrator sees the world through a single character's eyes and reveals that character's feelings and thoughts. The narrator can describe what other characters do or say but not what they feel or think.

A story's point of view affects what readers are told and what they must figure out. It may also affect which characters they identify or sympathize with and which characters they do not.

DIRECTIONS: *To understand point of view, readers must examine its effects on the telling of the story. It is sometimes useful to consider how a different point of view would affect the telling of the story. Answer the following questions to analyze the point of view in "Checkouts" and "The Girl Who Can."*

1. In "Checkouts," imagine that the author uses the first-person point of view with the girl as narrator. Review the description of the scene in which the bag boy drops and breaks the jar of mayonnaise. How would this scene be different if it were written from the first-person point of view?

   _____

   _____

   _____

   _____

   _____

2. Suppose that "The Girl Who Can" is told in the third-person omniscient point of view. Review the final scene in the story, in which Nana carries the trophy cup home on her back. How would this scene be different if it were told in the third-person omniscient point of view?

   _____

   _____

   _____

   _____

   _____

Name _____ Date _____

"Checkouts" by Cynthia Rylant
"The Girl Who Can" by Ama Ata Aidoo
Vocabulary Builder

Word List

reverie	dishevelment	perverse	fertile	comprehension	humble

A. DIRECTIONS: *Revise each sentence so that the underlined vocabulary word is used logically. Be sure not to change the vocabulary word.*

1. Sunk in <u>reverie</u>, the six-year-old twins had surprised expressions on their faces.

   _____

2. She brags endlessly about her accomplishments in a <u>humble</u> manner.

   _____

3. Hours of careful grooming resulted in Sam's state of <u>dishevelment</u> at the party.

   _____

4. May's sister took a <u>perverse</u> pleasure in making her laugh.

   _____

5. The soil is so extremely <u>fertile</u> that nothing can be grown in it.

   _____

B. DIRECTIONS: *Answer the following questions in the space provided.*

1. How would a person with a <u>humble</u> attitude behave?

   _____

   _____

2. Describe the appearance of a <u>fertile</u> piece of land.

   _____

   _____

   _____

3. How would you feel if you were sure of your <u>comprehension</u> of a complex topic?

   _____

   _____

Name _____ Date _____

"Checkouts" by Cynthia Rylant
"The Girl Who Can" by Ama Ata Aidoo
Writing to Compare Literary Works

Use a chart like the one below to make prewriting notes for your essay of comparison and contrast.

Points of Comparison/Contrast	"Checkouts"	"The Girl Who Can"
Who is the narrator in each story?		
What is the point of view?		
What do we learn of the thoughts and feelings of the girl and of Adjoa?		
How do other characters react to the girl and Adjoa?		

Name _____ Date _____

from *A White House Diary* by Lady Bird Johnson
Literary Analysis: Autobiographical Writing and Author's Voice

Voice is the way a writer sounds on the page. For example, the writer's voice in a work can be *smooth and sophisticated, choppy and blunt,* or *breathless and full of wonder.* Voice is a result of several elements:

- *word choice:* the kinds of words the writer uses
- *attitude:* the way the writer feels about his or her subject
- *sentence length and structure:* the arrangement of words and ideas in sentences

In **autobiographical writing,** the author tells all or part of his or her own life story. The kind of details that are included show what the writer notices, thinks, and feels about events. The voice of autobiographical writing usually reflects the writer's own personality and way of speaking.

In the following excerpt from *A White House Diary*, notice the words that seem to reveal feeling, and think about what they say about Mrs. Johnson's attitude toward her subject.

It's odd the little things that come to your mind at times of utmost stress, the flashes of deep compassion you feel for people who are really not at the center of the tragedy.

Words that reveal feelings: utmost stress, deep compassion, tragedy

Writer's attitude: All of these words help to show the depth of her very sad feelings.

DIRECTIONS: *Analyze the writer's voice in each passage. First, underline words that help reveal the writer's feelings. Then, tell what you think the writer's attitude is. Finally, tell what the syntax (sentence length and structure) reveals.*

1. We got in. Lyndon told the agents to stop the sirens. We drove along as fast as we could. I looked up at a building and there, already, was a flag at half-mast. I think that was when the enormity of what had happened first struck me.

   Words that reveal feelings: _____

   Writer's attitude: _____

   Syntax: _____

2. I looked at her. Mrs. Kennedy's dress was stained with blood. One leg was almost entirely covered with it and her right glove was caked, it was caked with blood—her husband's blood. Somehow that was one of the most poignant sights—that immaculate woman exquisitely dressed, and caked in blood.

   Words that reveal feelings: _____

   Writer's attitude: _____

   Syntax: _____

Name _____ Date _____

from *A White House Diary* by Lady Bird Johnson

Reading: Preview the Text to Identify an Author's Purpose

An **author's purpose** is his or her main reason for writing. An author writes for a general purpose, such as to inform, to entertain, or to persuade. He or she also writes for a specific purpose, such as to expose a particular problem in society. Before you read, **preview the text to look for an author's purpose.**

- Notice the focus of the title.
- Look for any organizing features, such as subheads.
- Identify the subject of photos, illustrations, or diagrams
- Read the first sentences of the opening paragraphs.

Make educated guesses about the author's purpose based on your preview. Later, as you read the full text, confirm whether your ideas are correct.

DIRECTIONS: *Preview the following opening paragraphs from an article. Then, answer the questions below.*

First Ladies Hall of Fame

Of course, there is no such thing as the First Ladies Hall of Fame, nor is there ever likely to be one. But if there were, two presidents' wives—Abigail Adams and Eleanor Roosevelt—would be among the first to be nominated.

A Legacy in Letters

Abigail Adams was the wife of the second President of the United States, John Adams. She was also the mother of the sixth President, John Quincy Adams. Fortunately, her letters to her husband and sister have been preserved. They are filled with details that provide an accurate, lively account of Colonial life during the Revolutionary period.

Her Childhood and Education

She was born Abigail Smith in Weymouth, Massachusetts in 1744. Both her mother's family and her father's were leaders during the Colonial period. Like the girls of her time, even wealthy ones, Abigail had no formal education. Abigail was an avid reader, however, and extremely curious about everything. It was partly her intelligence that attracted the young lawyer, John Adams, whom she married in 1764.

Her Major Accomplishments

During long separations from her husband, she managed the family farm and taught her children. (You may remember how she was vividly portrayed in the musical *1776*.)

1. Identify the author's purpose in this article. _____

_____

2. Identify the main subject or subjects of the article. _____

_____

3. When the author finishes writing about Abigail Adams, what will the author discuss next?

_____

_____

4. What does the title reveal about the author's attitude toward his subject? _____

_____

Name _____   Date _____

from *A White House Diary* by Lady Bird Johnson
Vocabulary Builder

Word List

tumultuous	implications	poignant

A. DIRECTIONS: *In each item below, think about the meaning of the italicized word, and then answer the question.*

1. Your school's basketball team is playing in the finals of the state championship. Describe what happens during the game to cause a *tumultuous* response from the fans.

_____

_____

2. Describe a *poignant* scene from a movie or TV show that you saw recently, and explain how you felt as you watched it.

_____

_____

_____

3. Your family will be moving to another state before school starts. Identify three of the *implications* of the move for you.

_____

_____

_____

B. DIRECTIONS: *Write the letter of the word or phrase that is the best synonym for the Word List word.*

____ 1. tumultuous
   A. in order
   B. in an uproar
   C. in a rage
   D. in surprise

____ 2. implications
   A. hints or suggestions
   B. signs or symbols
   C. important events
   D. indirect results

____ 3. poignant
   A. tense and exciting
   B. terrifying
   C. emotionally touching
   D. surprising

Name _____ Date _____

from *A White House Diary* by Lady Bird Johnson
Support for Writing a Journal Entry

Use the chart below to gather information for your **journal entry.** Write your ideas in complete sentences.

1. **Event:** _____

_____

2. **Check one:** ☐ **National** ☐ **Local** ☐ **Global significance** ☐ **Other** _____

3. **Who was affected by the event:** _____

_____

_____

4. **How they were affected:** _____

_____

_____

5. **How I felt during/about the event:** _____

_____

_____

6. **Specific words I associate with the event:** _____

_____

_____

7. **Specific images I remember about the event:** _____

_____

_____

_____

_____

Now, write your journal entry about the specific event and your response to it. As you describe the event, try to use the specific words and images you thought of, but feel free to add others.

Name _____ Date _____

"My English" by Julia Alvarez
Literary Analysis: Autobiographical Writing and Author's Voice

Voice is the way a writer sounds on the page. For example, the writer's voice in a work can be *smooth and sophisticated, choppy and blunt,* or *breathless and full of wonder.* Voice is a result of several elements:

- *word choice*: the kinds of words the writer uses
- *attitude*: the way the writer feels about his or her subject
- *sentence length and structure, or syntax*: the arrangement of words and ideas in sentences

In **autobiographical writing,** the author tells all or part of his or her own life story. The kind of details that are included show what the writer notices, thinks, and feels about events. The voice of autobiographical writing usually reflects the writer's own personality and way of speaking.

As you read an autobiography, notice the words that seem to reveal feeling. Think about what they say about Julia Alvarez's attitude toward her subject.

In sixth grade, I had one of the first in a lucky line of great English teachers who began to nurture in me a love of language, a love that had been there since my childhood of listening closely to words.

Words that reveal feelings: lucky, great, nurture, love

Writer's attitude: All of these words have positive connotations and help to show writer's great joy in using words.

DIRECTIONS: *Analyze the writer's voice in each passage. First, underline words that you think reveal something about the writer's voice. Then, tell what you think the writer's attitude is. Finally, tell what the syntax (sentence length and structure) reveals.*

1. Those women yakked as they cooked, they storytold, they gossiped, they sang—boleros, meringues, canciones, salves. Theirs were the voices that belonged to the rain and the wind and the teeny, teeny stars even a small child could blot out with her thumb.

   Word choice: _____

   Writer's attitude: _____

   Syntax: _____

2. *Butter, butter, butter, butter.* All day, one English word that had particularly struck me would go round and round in my mouth and weave through all the Spanish in my head until by the end of the day, the word did sound like just another Spanish word. And so I would say, "Mami, please pass la mantequilla." She would scowl and say in English, "I'm sorry, I don't understand. But would you be needing some butter on your bread?"

   Word choice: _____

   Writer's attitude: _____

   Syntax: _____

"My English" by Julia Alvarez
Reading: Preview the Text to Identify an Author's Purpose

An **author's purpose** is his or her main reason for writing. An author writes for a general purpose, such as to inform, to entertain or to persuade. He or she also writes for a specific purpose, such as to expose a particular problem in society. Before you read, **preview the text to look for an author's purpose.**

- Notice the focus of the title
- Look for any organizing features, like subheads
- Identify the subject of photos, illustrations, or diagrams
- Read the first sentences of the first few paragraphs

Make educated guesses about the author's purpose based on your preview. Later, as you read the full text, confirm whether your ideas are correct.

DIRECTIONS: *Preview the following opening paragraphs from an article. Then, answer the questions below.*

Evolving English

The one thing you can count on with a living language (one that is still in use) is that it changes. English has been changing since it first appeared as Old English about A.D. 500. Here are four ways in which English changes: new words, old words with new meanings, out-of-fashion words, and borrowed words.

New Words

Once these words did not exist: *cell phone, laptop, DVD player.* New words enter the English language when manufacturers invent names for their new products. Some people send new words they have made up to dictionary editors and try to sell them, but that is not how words are added to a language. They enter the language by being in common use.

Old Words With New Meanings

Another way language changes is by words taking on new meanings. *Memory*, for example, added a computer meaning when computers became common. Slang is another way that old words acquire new meanings. Long ago, *cool* simply meant the opposite of *warm*, but the slang meaning of *cool* has been around for a long time.

Out-of-Fashion Words

Dictionaries label some words as archaic or obsolete, which means they are no longer in common use. *Thee, prithee, whilst*, and *ere* are some examples of words that have disappeared.

1. Identify the author's purpose in this article. _____

    _____

2. Identify the main subject or subjects of the article. _____

    _____

3. When the author finishes writing about out-of-fashion words, what will the author discuss next? _____

    _____

Name _____ Date _____

"My English" by Julia Alvarez
Vocabulary Builder

Word List

bilingual	countenance	interminably

A. DIRECTIONS: *In each item below, think about the meaning of the italicized word, and then answer the question.*

1. Name three advantages of being *bilingual* in Spanish and English. _____
   _____
   _____

2. Describe your *countenance* when you discover that you have just won a million dollars on a TV game show.
   _____
   _____

3. How do you feel when you listen to a speech that goes on *interminably*?
   _____
   _____

B. DIRECTIONS: *Write the letter of the word or phrase that is the best synonym for the Word List word.*

____ 1. bilingual
    A. being confused
    B. having three languages
    C. using two languages
    D. learning new languages

____ 2. countenance
    A. face
    B. thoughts
    C. reaction
    D. feelings

____ 3. interminably
    A. excitedly
    B. terrifyingly
    C. emotionally
    D. endlessly

Name _____ Date _____

"My English" by Julia Alvarez
Support for Writing a Journal Entry

Use the chart below to gather information for your **journal entry.** Write your ideas in complete sentences.

1. My subject:
2. Why my subject is important to me:
3. When my subject first became important to me:
4. How I felt about my subject five years ago:
5. How I feel about my subject now:
6. Specific words I associate with my subject:
7. Specific images I associate with my subject:

Now, write your journal entry about a subject that is important to you. As you describe your subject, try to use the specific words and images you thought of, but feel free to add others.

from *A White House Diary* by Lady Bird Johnson
"My English" by Julia Alvarez
Build Language Skills: Vocabulary

The Latin Word Parts *tri-* and *via*

The **etymology** of a word is both its origin and the history of how the word has changed. For example, here is the etymology of the word *trivial:*

> trivial [L *trivialis*, of the crossroads, hence commonplace < *trivium*, place where three roads meet < *tri-*, TRI- + *via*, road: see VIA]

This etymology traces the word *trivial* all the way back to two Latin word parts: the prefix *tri-*, which means "three" and the root word *via*, which means "road." (The word *via* also means "way.") *Trivial* comes from a Latin word which means "the place where three roads meet—the crossroads or common place." Over the years *trivial* has come to mean "not important—common."

A. DIRECTIONS: *Using a dictionary, explain the origin of the underlined words. Then, write down the word's definition.*

1. Please set the hot plate on the <u>trivet</u>. _____

_____

2. In her workout today, she exercised her <u>triceps</u>. _____

_____

3. The Roman god Neptune is often shown with a <u>trident</u>. _____

_____

4. The train is traveling across a <u>viaduct</u> over the river. _____

_____

5. Her trans-Atlantic <u>voyage</u> will last five days. _____

_____

Academic Vocabulary Practice

B. DIRECTIONS: *Follow the instructions to write sentences containing the italicized academic vocabulary words.*

1. Use the word *vital* in a sentence about a character in a story. _____

_____

2. Tell two things that you *appreciate* most about your favorite author. _____

_____

3. Use the word *trivial* in a sentence about the details a writer chooses for a description. ___

_____

4. Use the verb *display* in a sentence about a supermarket. _____

_____

Name _____ Date _____

from **_A White House Diary_** by Lady Bird Johnson
"My English" by Julia Alvarez

Build Language Skills: Personal Pronouns

The most common pronouns are those that you use to refer to yourself and the people and things around you. These pronouns are called **personal pronouns.** Personal pronouns refer to the person speaking (first person), the person spoken to (second person), or the person, place, or thing spoken about (third person). Here is a chart of the personal pronouns.

	Singular	Plural
First Person	I, me, my, mine	we, us, our, ours
Second Person	you, your, yours	you, your, yours
Third Person	he, him, his; she, her, hers; it, its	they, them, their, theirs

The ending -*self* or -*selves* can be added to some personal pronouns to form reflexive and intensive pronouns. A **reflexive pronoun** indicates that someone or something performs an action to, for, or upon itself. Reflexive pronouns point back to a noun or pronoun earlier in the sentence. An **intensive pronoun** simply adds emphasis to a noun or pronoun in the same sentence. The eight reflexive and intensive pronouns are *myself, ourselves, yourself, yourselves, himself, herself, itself,* and *themselves.*

Reflexive Pronoun   She asked *herself* why everyone spoke English in New York.

Intensive Pronoun   I *myself* did not understand English as a child.

A. DIRECTIONS: *Underline all of the personal pronouns in these passages from "My English."*

1. Why my parents didn't first educate us in our native language by enrolling us in a Domini-can school, I don't know. Part of it was that Mami's family had a tradition of sending the boys to the States to boarding school and college, and she had been one of the first girls to be allowed to join her brothers. [You should find eight personal pronouns.]

2. There was also a neat little trick I wanted to try on an English-speaking adult at home. I had learned it from Elizabeth, my smart-alecky friend in fourth grade, whom I alternately worshiped and resented. [You should find five personal pronouns.]

B. DIRECTIONS: *You are planning to meet a pen pal, whom you have never seen before, in the train station. Write a short description of yourself so that your pen pal will recognize you. Use several personal pronouns and at least one example each of reflexive and intensive pronouns in your description. Then, underline the pronouns.*

_____

_____

_____

_____

"The Secret Life of Walter Mitty" by James Thurber
Literary Analysis: Character

A **character** is a person or an animal who takes part in the action of a literary work.

- A **round character** is complex, showing many different qualities—revealing faults as well as virtues. For example, a character might be honest but foolish, or dishonest but intelligent. A **flat character** is one-dimensional, showing only a single trait.
- A **dynamic character** develops, changes, and learns something during the course of a story, unlike a **static character,** who remains the same.

The main character of a story is almost always a round character and is usually dynamic. The main character's development and growth are often central to a story's plot and theme. As you read, consider the traits that make characters seem round or flat, dynamic or static.

DIRECTIONS: *For each numbered item, write a sentence telling what character trait or traits the passage reveals.*

1. **Mrs. Mitty:** "We've been all through that," she said, getting out of the car. "You're not a young man any longer." He raced the engine a little. "Why don't you wear your gloves? Have you lost your gloves?"

   Character traits of Mrs. Mitty: _____

   _____

2. **Walter Mitty:** Once he had tried to take his chains off [the tires], outside New Milford, and he had got them wound around the axles. A man had had to come out in a wrecking car and unwind them, a young, grinning garageman. Since then Mrs. Mitty always made him drive to a garage to have the chains taken off. The next time, he thought, I'll wear my right arm in a sling; they won't grin at me then.

   Character traits of Walter Mitty: _____

   _____

3. **Walter Mitty:** A woman's scream rose above the bedlam and suddenly a lovely, dark-haired girl was in Walter Mitty's arms. The District Attorney struck at her savagely. Without rising from his chair, Mitty let the man have it on the point of the chin. "You miserable cur!"

   Character traits of Walter Mitty: _____

   _____

4. **Mrs. Mitty and Walter Mitty:** "Did you get the what's-its-name? The puppy biscuit? What's in that box?" "Overshoes," said Mitty. "Couldn't you have put them on in the store?" "I was thinking," said Walter Mitty. "Does it ever occur to you that I am sometimes thinking?" She looked at him. "I'm going to take your temperature when I get you home," she said.

   Character traits of Mrs. Mitty and Walter Mitty: _____

   _____

Name _____ Date _____

"The Secret Life of Walter Mitty" by James Thurber

Reading: Reflect on Details and Events to Determine an Author's Purpose

An **author's purpose** is his or her main reason for writing. In fiction, the specific purpose is often to convey the story's theme, message, or insight. Pause periodically while reading and **reflect** on the story's details and events to determine the author's purpose. Ask questions such as, *What significance might this event have?* or *Why does the author include this detail?* Based on your reflections, formulate ideas about what the author's purpose might be.

DIRECTIONS: *Write one or two sentences telling why, in your opinion, James Thurber might have included each of the following details or events in "The Secret Life of Walter Mitty."*

1. Mrs. Mitty scolds her husband for driving too fast and for not wearing his gloves. He does what she tells him to do.

   _____

   _____

2. Walter Mitty daydreams, imagining that he is an important surgeon who repairs a piece of medical equipment and saves a patient's life.

   _____

   _____

3. Walter Mitty tells his wife that he does not need overshoes, but his wife insists that he does. He buys the overshoes.

   _____

   _____

4. Walter Mitty daydreams, imagining that he is a heroic air force captain about to fly a two-man bomber into heavy combat by himself.

   _____

   _____

5. Walter Mitty daydreams, imagining himself heroically facing a firing squad—"proud and disdainful, Walter Mitty the Undefeated, inscrutable to the last."

   _____

   _____

   _____

"The Secret Life of Walter Mitty" by James Thurber
Vocabulary Builder

Word List

| distraught | insolent | inscrutable |

A. DIRECTIONS: *Read each sentence, and think about the meaning of the italicized Word List word. Then, answer the question. Use the vocabulary word in your answer.*

1. Describe two situations that might cause someone to feel *distraught*.

   _____

   _____

2. In your opinion, how should the manager of a team react to an athlete's *insolent* behavior?

   _____

   _____

3. *Mona Lisa*, a portrait by Leonardo da Vinci, is famous for the subject's *inscrutable* smile. Describe someone with an inscrutable expression. How does the person look? Why is the expression inscrutable?

   _____

   _____

   _____

B. DIRECTIONS: *Each item consists of a related pair of words in CAPITAL LETTERS followed by four pairs of words. Write the letter of the pair that best expresses a relationship similar to the one expressed by the pair of words in capital letters.*

_____ 1. INSOLENT : RESPECTFUL ::
   A. ancient : old
   B. backward : forward
   C. curious : eager
   D. incredible : unbelievable

_____ 2. INSCRUTABLE : PUZZLING ::
   A. tardy : early
   B. precise : careless
   C. circular : round
   D. energetic : exhausted

_____ 3. DISTRAUGHT : CAREFREE ::
   A. dangerous : treacherous
   B. alien : stranger
   C. mammoth : enormous
   D. casual : formal

Name _____ Date _____

"The Secret Life of Walter Mitty" by James Thurber
Support for Writing a Character Profile

Choose one of the heroic characters in Walter Mitty's daydreams (Commander of a navy seaplane, famous surgeon, defendant at a trial, or Captain of a bomber). Gather ideas for your **character profile** by completing this cluster diagram.

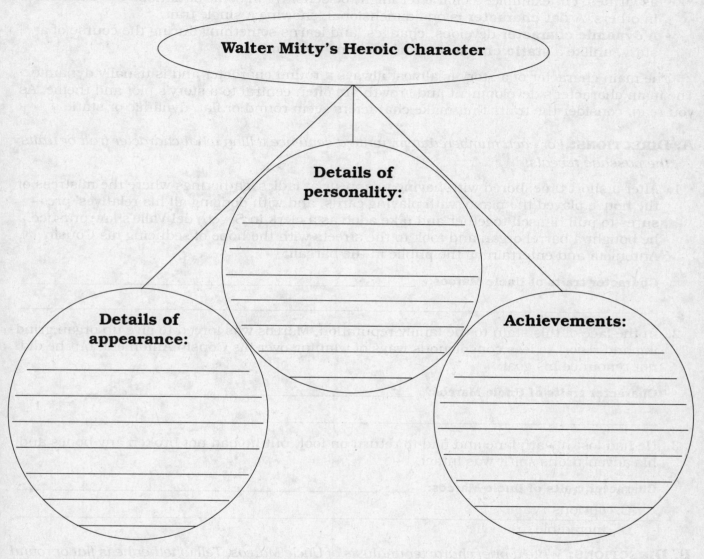

1. What single impression of the character do you want to convey?
   _____

2. Place a check mark next to the details in your diagram that will help you convey that impression.

3. Briefly list ideas in the order in which you will present them in your character profile.
   _____
   _____

Now, use your notes to draft a character profile of one of Walter Mitty's heroic personalities.

Name _____ Date _____

"Uncle Marcos" from *The House of the Spirits* by Isabel Allende
Literary Analysis: Character

A **character** is a person or an animal who takes part in the action of a literary work.

- A **round character** is complex, showing many different qualities—revealing faults as well as virtues. For example, a character might be sensitive in some situations but insensitive in others. A **flat character** is one-dimensional, showing a single trait.
- A **dynamic character** develops, changes, and learns something during the course of a story, unlike a **static character,** who remains the same.

The main character of a story is almost always a round character and is usually dynamic. The main character's development and growth are often central to a story's plot and theme. As you read, consider the traits that make characters seem round or flat, dynamic or static.

A. DIRECTIONS: *For each numbered item, write a sentence telling what character trait or traits the passage reveals.*

1. After a short time, bored with having to appear at ladies' gatherings where the mistress of the house played the piano, with playing cards, and with dodging all his relatives' pressures to pull himself together and take a job as a clerk in Severo del Valle's law practice, he bought a barrel organ and took to the streets with the hope of seducing his Cousin Antonieta and entertaining the public in the bargain.

   Character traits of Uncle Marcos: _____

   _____

2. In the face of this stain to the family reputation, Marcos was forced to give up organ grinding and resort to less conspicuous ways of winning over his Cousin Antonieta, but he did not renounce his goal.

   Character traits of Uncle Marcos: _____

   _____

3. He had lost his airplane and had to return on foot, but he had not broken any bones and his adventurous spirit was intact.

   Character traits of Uncle Marcos: _____

   _____

B. DIRECTIONS: *Write a brief character analysis of Uncle Marcos. Tell whether he is flat or round and dynamic or static. Give examples from the story to support your statements.*

_____

_____

_____

_____

_____

_____

Name _____ Date _____

Reading: Reflect on Details and Events to Determine an Author's Purpose

An **author's purpose** is his or her main reason for writing. In fiction, the specific purpose is often to convey the story's theme, message, or insight. Pause periodically while reading and **reflect** on the story's details and events to determine the author's purpose. Ask questions such as, *What significance might this event have?* or *Why does the author include this detail?*

Based on your reflections, formulate ideas about what the author's purpose might be.

A. DIRECTIONS: *Write one or two sentences telling why, in your opinion, Isabel Allende might have included each of the following details or events in "Uncle Marcos."*

1. Uncle Marcos sleeps during the day, stays up all night, and performs strange experiments in the kitchen.

_____

_____

2. He refuses to take a job in his brother-in-law's law firm.

_____

_____

3. He embarrasses the family by serenading Cousin Antonieta with a barrel-organ and a parrot.

_____

_____

4. He builds an airplane and takes off in it.

_____

_____

5. He gives up the fortune-telling business when he realizes that it is affecting people's lives.

_____

_____

B. DIRECTIONS: *Think back over the events and details of the story and your answers to the questions above. Then, in a sentence or two, write what you think the author's purpose is in "Uncle Marcos."*

_____

_____

_____

Name _____   Date _____

"Uncle Marcos" from *The House of the Spirits* by Isabel Allende
Vocabulary Builder

Word List

pallid   disconsolately   unrequited

A. DIRECTIONS: *Read each sentence, and think about the meaning of the italicized Word List word. Then, answer the question. Use the vocabulary word in your answer.*

1. Describe a situation in which someone does something *disconsolately*. What might the person be doing? How does he or she feel?

   _____

   _____

2. Under what circumstances might a person look *pallid*? How might he or she look?

   _____

   _____

3. If someone knows for sure that his or her feelings for another person are *unrequited*, what might the person do? (Uncle Marcos set off on a trip around the world.)

   _____

   _____

B. DIRECTIONS: *Each item consists of a related pair of words in CAPITAL LETTERS followed by four pairs of words. Write the letter of the pair that best expresses a relationship similar to the one expressed by the pair in capital letters.*

____ 1. PALLID : PALE ::
   A. tense : relaxed
   B. organized : messy
   C. anxious : worried
   D. stubborn : mule

____ 2. JOYFULLY : DISCONSOLATELY ::
   A. methodically : carefully
   B. overflowing : empty
   C. static : unchanged
   D. common : familiar

____ 3. UNREQUITED : RETURNED ::
   A. tamed : wild
   B. wrinkled : rumpled
   C. tiny : molecule
   D. exceptional : unusual

Name _____ Date _____

Support for Writing a Character Profile

Gather ideas for your **character profile** of Uncle Marcos by completing this cluster diagram.

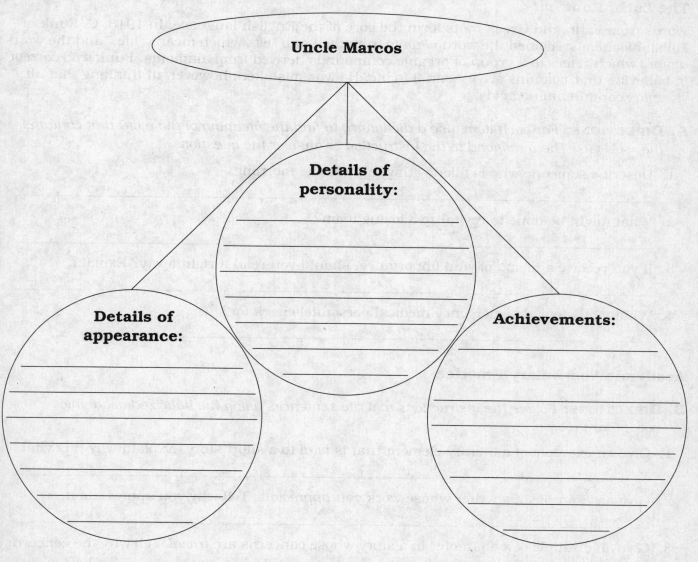

1. What single impression of Uncle Marcos do you want to convey?

_____

_____

2. Place a check mark next to the details in your diagram that will help you convey that impression.

3. Briefly list ideas in the order in which you will present them in your character profile.

_____

_____

_____

Now, use your notes to draft a character profile of Uncle Marcos.

45

"The Secret Life of Walter Mitty" by James Thurber
"Uncle Marcos" from **The House of the Spirits** by Isabel Allende
Build Language Skills: Vocabulary

The Latin Root -vit-

Words from Latin and Greek roots form the core of the English language. In 1913, C. Funk, a Polish biochemist, coined the word *vitamin* from the Latin *-vit-*, which means "life," and the word *amine*, which refers to a group of organic compounds derived from ammonia. Funk was correct in believing that *vit*amins are essential to life. He was mistaken, however, in thinking that all vit*amins* contain amino acids.

A. DIRECTIONS: *For each item, use a dictionary to find the meaning of the word that contains the root -vit-. Then, respond to the instruction or answer the question.*

1. Describe someone who is filled with <u>vitality</u> in the morning.

   _____

2. What might be done to <u>revitalize</u> a losing team?

   _____

3. If you receive a memo of <u>vital</u> importance, should you read it right away? Explain.

   _____

4. What <u>vital signs</u> do emergency medical personnel check for?

   _____

Academic Vocabulary Practice

B. DIRECTIONS: *Follow the instructions to write sentences using the italicized academic vocabulary words.*

1. Give an example of a literary element that is *vital* to a short story. Explain why it is vital.

   _____

2. Give an example of a writer whose work you *appreciate*. Tell why you appreciate it.

   _____

3. Give an example of a character in a story whose concerns are *trivial*. Tell why the concerns are trivial.

   _____

4. Give an example of a character trait that either Walter Mitty or Uncle Marcos can be said to *display*.

   _____

5. In fiction, how does a writer help you *detect* what a character is really like?

   _____

"The Secret Life of Walter Mitty" by James Thurber
"Uncle Marcos" from **The House of the Spirits** by Isabel Allende

Build Language Skills: Grammar

Relative, Interrogative, and Indefinite Pronouns

Pronouns are words that stand for nouns or for words that take the place of nouns. There are a number of different kinds of pronouns.

A **relative pronoun** begins a subordinate clause and connects it to another idea in the sentence. The five relative pronouns are *that, which, who, whom,* and *whose.*

Uncle Marcos is a person *who* likes adventure.

An **interrogative pronoun** begins a question. The five interrogative pronouns are *what, which, who, whom,* and *whose.*

Who is Clara?

Indefinite pronouns refer to people, places, or things, often without specifying which ones. Words that are or can function as indefinite pronouns include *anyone, everybody, nobody,* and *somebody; anything, nothing,* and *something; any, all, few, many, most, one,* and *some; little* and *much;* and *another, both,* and *either.*

Everybody came out to watch Uncle Marcos take off in the airplane.

A. PRACTICE: *Underline the relative, interrogative, or indefinite pronoun in each sentence. On the line or lines following the sentence, identify each pronoun you underlined as* relative, interrogative, *or* indefinite.

1. Trunks, animals in jars of formaldehyde, and Indian lances are some of the items that Uncle Marcos brought home from his travels. _____, _____

2. In whose house did Marcos spend his time, sleeping during the day and conducting experiments at night? _____

3. Marcos's departure by airplane was a remarkable event, which virtually everyone in town had come out to witness. _____, _____

4. Who were the explorers and mountain climbers who claimed to have found the body? _____, _____

5. Everyone was saddened when they appeared with the coffin that they claimed held Uncle Marcos's body (but which actually contained bags of sand). _____, _____, _____

B. Writing Application: *Write a paragraph that summarizes what happens when Uncle Marcos courts Cousin Antonieta. Use at least one relative pronoun, one interrogative pronoun, and one indefinite pronoun in your paragraph, and underline each.*

_____

_____

_____

_____

_____

"If I Forget Thee, Oh Earth . . ." by Arthur C. Clarke
from **Silent Spring** by Rachel Carson
Literary Analysis: Theme

The **theme** of a literary work is the central message or insight about life that is conveyed through the work. Sometimes, the theme is stated directly. More often, it is suggested indirectly through the words and experiences of the characters or through the events of a story.

How theme is developed depends in part on the genre, or form, of the work. In nonfiction literature, such as essays, the theme is usually stated directly as a main idea. Then, the writer supports the idea with facts, details, and examples to prove the point.

In most fiction—short stories, novels, poetry, and plays—the theme is implied, or suggested. Readers must figure out the theme by looking at the ideas expressed through story events and character actions.

DIRECTIONS: *Read the following passages and describe how each passage relates to the selection's theme.*

from "If I Forget Thee, Oh Earth . . ."

He was looking upon the funeral pyre of a world—upon the radioactive aftermath of Armageddon. Across a quarter of a million miles of space, the glow of dying atoms was still visible, a perennial reminder of the ruinous past. It would be centuries yet before that deadly glow died from the rocks and life could return again to fill that silent, empty world.

1. What does this passage imply about what has happened to Earth?

_____

2. How does this passage relate to the theme of the story?

_____

3. How would you state the theme of this story?

_____

from *Silent Spring*

In the gutters under the eaves and between the shingles of the roofs, a white granular powder still showed a few patches; some weeks before it had fallen like snow upon the roofs and lawns, the fields and streams.

No witchcraft, no enemy action had silenced the rebirth of new life in this stricken world. The people had done it themselves.

1. What might the "white granular powder" be? What are the effects of the powder?

_____

2. How does this passage relate to the theme of the selection?

_____

3. How would you state the theme of this selection?

_____

Name _____   Date _____

"If I Forget Thee, Oh Earth . . ." by Arthur C. Clarke
from Silent Spring by Rachel Carson
Vocabulary Builder

Word List

| purged   perennial   blight   maladies   moribund |

A. DIRECTIONS: *Revise each sentence so that the underlined vocabulary word is used logically. Be sure not to change the vocabulary word.*

1. I <u>purged</u> the wound on my foot, thereby increasing the chances of infection.

   _____

2. Those flowers are <u>perennial</u>, so you will need to plant them again next year.

   _____

3. Because of the <u>blight</u>, the potatoes we grew were especially fine this year.

   _____

4. Due to various <u>maladies</u>, they became more vigorous and cheerful.

   _____

5. The fact that her garden was <u>moribund</u> filled her with delight.

   _____

B. DIRECTIONS: *Write the letter of the word or phrase that is the best synonym for the Word List word.*

___ **1.** perennial
   A. occasional
   B. temporary
   C. perpetual
   D. unusual

___ **2.** maladies
   A. complaints
   B. diseases
   C. mistakes
   D. theories

___ **3.** moribund
   A. depressing
   B. upsetting
   C. cheering
   D. dying

___ **4.** purged
   A. cleansed
   B. destroyed
   C. manufactured
   D. created

Name _____ Date _____

"If I Forget Thee, Oh Earth . . ." by Arthur C. Clarke
from Silent Spring by Rachel Carson
Writing to Compare Literary Works

Use a chart like the one below to make prewriting notes for your essay of comparison and contrast. Then, answer the two questions following the chart.

Points of Comparison/Contrast	"If I Forget Thee . . ."	from *Silent Spring*
My response to each selection		
Statement of each selection's theme		
Possible reasons why author chose genre		

1. In general, do you think fiction or nonfiction is more effective in expressing a theme? Explain.

   _____

   _____

   _____

2. Which of these two selections do you think is more effective in expressing its theme? Explain.

   _____

   _____

   _____

Name _____ Date _____

Wayson Choy
Listening and Viewing

Segment 1: Meet Wayson Choy
- How did Wayson Choy's experience growing up in Chinatown influence his writing?
- In what way are Choy's stories a bridge between two worlds?

_____

_____

_____

_____

Segment 2: The Short Story
- What do windchimes symbolize in "The Jade Peony"?
- Why would a writer build a short story around a symbol?

_____

_____

_____

_____

Segment 3: The Writing Process
- According to Wayson Choy, how is the process of a caterpillar turning into a butterfly similar to the writing process?
- How is your writing process similar to the process Choy describes?

_____

_____

_____

_____

Segment 4: The Rewards of Writing
- According Wayson Choy, literature is important to all people.
- Why does he think that?
- What have you learned from or identified with in a particular piece of literature?

_____

_____

_____

_____

Name _____ Date _____

Unit 2
Learning About Short Stories

A **short story** is a work of fiction meant to be read in one sitting. It is crafted in a concise manner so that it accomplishes its purpose in relatively few words—usually 500 to 10,000.

The **plot** is the series of related events that take place in the story. During the course of the plot, events unfold. They build to a **climax** (the point of greatest tension, or the turning point) and then, during the **resolution,** come to a conclusion.

At the core of the plot is a **conflict,** or struggle. An **external conflict** occurs between characters, between an individual and a group, or between a character and a force of nature. An **internal conflict** takes place within the mind of a character.

The **characters,** the personalities who participate in the action, are usually human beings, but they may be animals or even objects. Characters are described by means of **characterization:** descriptions of characters' appearance and actions, dialogue in which characters interact with other characters and reveal information about themselves and others, and descriptions of characters' thoughts and feelings.

The **setting** is the time and place of the action. It may be the past, the present, or the future. It may be unspecific, or it may name a particular season, year, or even hour of the day. It may refer to a social, an economic, or a cultural environment, and it may specify a geographic location—a country, town, or neighborhood. The setting sets the stage for the action. It may also create a mood or an atmosphere or present a character with a conflict.

The **theme** is a story's central message or insight into life. A **stated theme** is expressed directly by the author. An implied theme is suggested by the experiences of the characters or the events and the setting of the work.

DIRECTIONS: *Write the letter of the short-story element that best describes each numbered item.*

____ 1. A freestyle swimmer finishes in first-place at an important meet.
  A. setting   B. character   C. climax

____ 2. A woman struggles against discrimination at her job.
  A. setting   B. conflict   C. resolution

____ 3. Two rivals grow to admire each other.
  A. plot   B. climax   C. resolution

____ 4. A neighborhood in San Francisco's Chinatown is described.
  A. setting   B. character   C. theme

____ 5. An obscure individual longs to become powerful and respected.
  A. internal conflict   B. external conflict   C. resolution

____ 6. A young person learns that self-confidence is a powerful quality.
  A. character   B. setting   C. theme

____ 7. A research station in Antarctica is described.
  A. theme   B. plot   C. setting

____ 8. An elderly woman recalls a long-lost love.
  A. characterization   B. theme   C. resolution

____ 9. A grandfather teaches his grandson about the respect owed to all creatures.
  A. climax   B. theme   C. characterization

52

"The Jade Peony" by Wayson Choy
Model Selection: Short Story

The **plot** of a short story is the series of related events that take place in the course of the story. At the core of a story's plot is usually a **conflict,** or struggle. The conflict may be **external,** in which case it features a clash between the main character and another character, between the main character and a group or society as a whole, or between the main character and a force of nature. If the conflict is **internal,** the struggle takes place within the character's mind.

The conflicts in a story typically build to a **climax,** or turning point. The events following the climax make up the outcome of the story, or the **resolution.**

Writers of short stories use methods of **characterization** to show what the characters are like. For example, writers may describe the characters' appearance and actions, quote their words, show them interacting with other characters, and describe their thoughts and feelings.

Another essential element of a short story is its setting. The **setting** is the time and place of the action. It may be general or specific, and it may include the social, economic, or cultural environment. Sometimes, the setting contributes to the **atmosphere,** or overall emotional mood, of a story. Sometimes, the setting creates a conflict.

A story's **theme** is its central message or insight about life. A **stated theme** is directly expressed by the writer. An **implied theme** is suggested by the characters' experiences, the setting, the author's tone or attitude, and/or the style of the work as a whole.

DIRECTIONS: *On the lines provided, answer these questions about "The Jade Peony."*

1. What conflicts, or problems, does Grandmama face?

   _____

   _____

2. What conflicts, or problems, does Sek-Lung (the narrator) face?

   _____

   _____

3. What conflicts, or problems, do the other members of the family face?

   _____

   _____

4. What is the setting of the story? _____

   _____

5. What role does the cultural environment play? _____

   _____

6. What is the climax of the story? Explain your answer. _____

   _____

   _____

7. In your opinion, what is the story's message about life and behavior?

   _____

   _____

Name _____ Date _____

"American History" by Judith Ortiz Cofer
Literary Analysis: Conflict

Conflict is a struggle between opposing forces. There are two types of conflict: internal and external.

- In **internal conflict,** a character struggles with his or her own opposing feelings, beliefs, needs, or desires.
- In **external conflict,** a character struggles against an outside force, such as another character, society, or nature.

Conflict and the search for a solution are the mainspring of a story's plot. The solution, which usually occurs near the end of a story, is called the **resolution.** In some stories, the conflict is not truly resolved. Instead, the main character experiences an **epiphany,** or sudden flash of insight. Although the conflict is not resolved, the character's thoughts about it change.

A. DIRECTIONS: *"American History" contains a number of conflicts. On the following lines, briefly describe the story situation surrounding each conflict.*

1. Elena vs. Gail _____

   _____

2. Elena and Eugene vs. their classmates _____

   _____

3. Elena vs. her mother _____

   _____

4. Elena within herself _____

   _____

5. Elena vs. Eugene's mother _____

   _____

B. DIRECTIONS: *On the following lines, briefly discuss the story's ending. Does the ending contain a resolution that solves the story's main conflict, or does it contain an epiphany, a sudden flash of insight? Explain your answer by citing details from the story.*

_____

_____

_____

_____

_____

_____

Name _____   Date _____

"American History" by Judith Ortiz Cofer
Reading: Use Details to Make Inferences

An **inference** is a logical guess that you make based on details in a story. When you make inferences, you read between the lines to understand information that is not stated directly. To make inferences, ask yourself questions about the feelings and behavior of the characters. Here are some helpful questions to ask:

- What does this detail show about a character's motivation, or the reasons for his or her behavior?
- What does this passage say about the character's unspoken feelings and thoughts?

Detail from the story: But the day President Kennedy was shot there was a profound silence in El Building.

Inference: The residents of El Building are deeply shocked by the assassination of President Kennedy.

DIRECTIONS: *Use the following chart to make inferences about the characters' motivations and feelings from the details listed. The first item has been done for you.*

Details in the Story	My Inferences About Motivations/ Feelings
1. There was only one source of beauty and light for me that school year.	Elena likes Eugene very much.
2. Eugene was in honors classes for all his subjects; classes that were not open to me because English was not my first language, though I was a straight A student.	
3. Since I had turned fourteen . . . my mother had been more vigilant than ever.	
4. "You are going out today?" The way she said 'today' sounded as if a storm warning had been issued.	
5. "You live there?" She pointed up to El Building, which looked particularly ugly, like a gray prison with its many dirty windows and rusty fire escapes.	

Name _____ Date _____

"American History" by Judith Ortiz Cofer
Vocabulary Builder

Word List

tenement	profound	vigilant	dilapidated

A. DIRECTIONS: *For each of the following items, think about the meaning of the italicized word, and then answer the question.*

1. How does a typical *tenement* look—elegant or run-down? _____

   _____

2. If your aunt expresses *profound* misgivings about moving to Puerto Rico, how does she feel about the move? _____

   _____

3. If a watchdog is *vigilant,* is the dog doing its job well or badly? Explain. _____

   _____

4. If you want to move into a house in good condition, would you be likely to choose a *dilapidated* one? Explain why or why not. _____

   _____

B. DIRECTIONS: *For each of the following items, write a single sentence in which you use the words as grouped.*

1. *dilapidated, tenement, profound*

   _____

   _____

2. *discreet* and *vigilant*

   _____

   _____

"American History" by Judith Ortiz Cofer
Support for Writing an Alternative Ending

For your alternative ending to "American History," use the following lines to jot down notes under each heading.

1. New ending grows out of earlier sequence of events:

Elena's life at school → Elena's attraction to Eugene → Mother's warnings → Study date with Eugene → Assassination of President Kennedy → _____

_____

_____

_____

2. New ending is consistent with portrayal of characters:

Elena's character traits: _____

_____

Personality of Elena's mother: _____

_____

Eugene's character traits: _____

_____

Personality of Eugene's mother: _____

_____

3. New ending provides a resolution to the conflict:

_____

_____

_____

_____

_____

_____

_____

Now, use your notes to write an alternative ending to "American History." Write your ending on a separate piece of paper. Be sure that your new ending resolves the main conflict in the story.

Name _____   Date _____

"The Most Dangerous Game" by Richard Connell
Literary Analysis: Conflict

Conflict is a struggle between opposing forces. There are two types of conflict: internal and external.

- In **internal conflict,** a character struggles with his or her own opposing feelings, beliefs, needs, or desires.
- In **external conflict,** a character struggles against an outside force, such as another character, society, or nature.

Conflict and the search for a solution are the mainspring of a story's plot. The solution, which usually occurs near the end of a story, is called the **resolution.** In some stories, the conflict is not truly resolved. Instead, the main character experiences an **epiphany,** or sudden flash of insight. Although the conflict is not resolved, the character's thoughts about it change.

A. DIRECTIONS: *"The Most Dangerous Game" contains a number of conflicts. On the following lines, briefly describe the story situations surrounding each conflict.*

1. Rainsford vs. nature _____

_____

_____

2. General Zaroff vs. the "visitors" to his island _____

_____

_____

3. Rainsford vs. General Zaroff _____

_____

_____

4. Rainsford within himself _____

_____

_____

B. DIRECTIONS: *On the following lines, briefly discuss the story's ending. Does the ending contain a resolution that solves the story's main conflict? Have Rainsford's experiences changed his views about hunting? Explain your answer by citing details from the story.*

_____

_____

_____

_____

_____

_____

"The Most Dangerous Game" by Richard Connell

Reading: Use Details to Make Inferences

An **inference** is a logical guess that you make based on details in a story. When you make inferences, you read between the lines to understand information that is not stated directly. To make inferences, ask yourself questions about the feelings and behavior of the characters. Here are some helpful questions to ask.

- What does this detail show about a character's motivation, or the reasons for his or her behavior?
- What does this passage say about the character's unspoken feelings and thoughts?

Example from "The Most Dangerous Game":

Detail from the story: "I can't believe you are serious, General Zaroff. This is a grisly joke."

Inference: Rainsford has just begun to realize that Zaroff hunts humans.

A. DIRECTIONS: *Use the following chart to make inferences from the details listed. The first item has been done for you.*

Details in the Story	My Inferences About Motivations/ Feelings
1. Rainsford tells Whitney that there are only two classes of people: hunters and huntees.	Rainsford begins the story with a matter-of-fact, almost hard-boiled attitude.
2. Rainsford asks Zaroff to excuse him for the night because he feels sick.	
3. Zaroff tells Rainsford how upset he was at the death of his dog Lazarus.	
4. Rainsford is able to rig up several ingenious traps, such as the Burmese tiger pit and a Malay mancatcher.	

B. DIRECTIONS: *Do you think "The Most Dangerous Game" has a serious theme, or message about human nature or behavior? Or, is it primarily a suspenseful adventure story intended to entertain readers rather than to make a point? Explain your answer with specific references to details in the story.*

_____

_____

_____

Name _____ Date _____

"The Most Dangerous Game" by Richard Connell
Vocabulary Builder

Word List

palpable	indolently	scruples	futile

A. DIRECTIONS: *In each of the following items, think about the meaning of the italicized word, and then answer the question.*

1. What is the danger if you approach a research paper assignment *indolently*?

_____

_____

2. How are you feeling if you have *scruples* about doing something?

_____

_____

3. How would you feel if you make a long and *futile* journey?

_____

_____

4. If the tension during the final two minutes of a game is *palpable*, do you think the spectators feel suspense or not? Explain.

_____

B. DIRECTIONS: *For each of the following items, write a single sentence in which you use the words as grouped.*

1. *palpable* and *scruples*

_____

_____

2. *indolently* and *futile*

_____

_____

Name _____ Date _____

"The Most Dangerous Game" by Richard Connell
Support for Writing an Alternative Ending

For your alternative ending to "The Most Dangerous Game," use the following lines to jot down notes under each heading.

1. New ending grows out of earlier sequence of events:

Rainsford falls off yacht and lands on island →Rainsford meets General Zaroff and learns of Zaroff's "game" →Rainsford is forced to become the "huntee" →Rainsford confronts Zaroff in the general's bedroom → _____

_____

_____

2. New ending is consistent with portrayal of characters:

Rainsford's character traits: _____

_____

Zaroff's character traits: _____

_____

3. New ending provides a resolution to the conflict:

_____

_____

_____

_____

_____

_____

_____

_____

Now, use your notes to write an alternative ending to "The Most Dangerous Game." Write your ending on a separate piece of paper. Be sure that your new ending resolves the main conflict in the story.

"American History" by Judith Ortiz Cofer
"The Most Dangerous Game" by Richard Connell
Build Language Skills: Vocabulary

Word Roots -spec-,-circum-

The Latin root -spec- means "to look" or "to see." This root appears in English words that have to do with "looking at," "looking upon," or "seeing" something. For example, when you discuss an *aspect* of a story, you look at a particular part or feature. When you *inspect* something, you look at it carefully.

The Latin root -circum- means "around" or "surrounding." A *circumstance* is a fact or an event that surrounds another event. To *circumvent* a difficulty or an obstacle is to find a way around it.

A. DIRECTIONS: *Use a dictionary to look up the origin of each of the following words containing the roots -spec- and -circum-. Write one meaning for each word. Then, write a sentence in which you use the word in a context that makes its meaning clear.*

1. speculate Meaning: _____

   Sentence: _____

2. specter Meaning: _____

   Sentence: _____

3. circumlocution Meaning: _____

   Sentence: _____

4. circumscribe Meaning: _____

   Sentence: _____

Academic Vocabulary Practice

B. DIRECTIONS: *Answer each question using the underlined academic vocabulary word.*

1. Do appeals to <u>emotion</u> usually involve the head more than the heart or vice versa?

   _____

2. What is one way you can <u>categorize</u> the characters in a story or play?

   _____

3. What literary <u>element</u> do writers use to describe the circumstances of a story, such as the time and place that the events occur?

   _____

4. What elements in a story often serve as clues to a character's <u>motives</u>?

   _____

5. Why is the point of view usually an important <u>aspect</u> of a story?

   _____

Name _____ Date _____

"American History" by Judith Ortiz Cofer
"The Most Dangerous Game" by Richard Connell
Build Language Skills: Grammar

Regular Verbs

A verb has four principal parts: the present, the present participle, the past, and the past participle. Most verbs in English are regular. **Regular verbs** form the past and the past participle by adding *-ed* or *-d* to the present form.

The past and past participle of regular verbs have the same form. In the following chart of principal parts, *has* is in parentheses in front of the past participle to remind you that this verb form is a past participle only if it is used with a helping verb.

Notice that the final consonant is sometimes doubled to form the present participle (*tapping*) as well as the past and the past participle (*tapped*). Notice also that the final *e* may be dropped in forming the present participle (*wiping*).

Principal Parts of Regular Verbs			
Present	**Present Participle**	**Past**	**Past Participle**
play	(is) playing	played	(has) played
tap	(is) tapping	tapped	(has) tapped
wipe	(is) wiping	(is) wiped	(has) wiped

A. PRACTICE: *Write the answer(s) to each of the following questions on the lines provided.*

1. Give the four principal parts of the following verbs:

   walk: _____

   hunt: _____

   place: _____

   rip: _____

2. What do you add to form the past tense of regular verbs? _____

B. Writing Application: *Read the following sentences and notice the verb in italics. If the verb is used correctly, write* Correct *in the space provided. If the verb is not used correctly, rewrite the sentence using the correct form of the verb.*

1. In Paterson, New Jersey, Elena *lived* in El Building with her family.

   _____

2. After school started, Elena *looking* for Eugene in all her classes.

   _____

3. Mr. DePalma has *ask* us to line up in front of him.

   _____

4. Rainsford was exhausted when he *arrive* on the island.

   _____

"The Gift of the Magi" by O. Henry
Literary Analysis: Irony and Surprise Ending

Irony is a difference or a contradiction between appearance and reality or between what is expected and what actually happens.

- In **situational irony,** something happens in the story that directly contradicts the expectations of a character or the reader. For example, you would expect that if Jim works hard at his job for a year, he will get a raise. If he gets a pay cut instead, the situation is ironic.
- A **surprise ending** often helps to create situational irony through a turn of events that takes the reader by surprise. To make a surprise ending believable, the author builds clues into the story that make the ending logical.

A. DIRECTIONS: *For each of the following excerpts from "The Gift of the Magi," write* **I** *in the space provided if the excerpt is ironic. Write* **N** *if the excerpt is not ironic. On the lines following each item, briefly explain why the excerpt is or is not ironic.*

____ 1. "Tomorrow would be Christmas Day, and she had only $1.87 with which to buy Jim a present. She had been saving every penny she could for months, with this result."

_____

_____

____ 2. "Where she stopped the sign read: 'Mme. Sofronie. Hair Goods of All Kinds.' One flight up Della ran, and collected herself, panting. Madame, large, too white, chilly, hardly looked the 'Sofronie.'"

_____

_____

____ 3. "Grand as the watch was he sometimes looked at it on the sly on account of the old leather strap that he used in place of a chain."

_____

_____

____ 4. "They were expensive combs, she knew, and her heart had simply craved and yearned over them without the least hope of possession. And now they were hers, but the tresses that should have adorned the coveted adornments were gone."

_____

_____

B. DIRECTIONS: *On the following lines, briefly explain the surprise ending in "The Gift of the Magi." Then, explain how O. Henry makes the surprise ending seem logical.*

_____

_____

_____

_____

_____

"The Gift of the Magi" by O. Henry

Reading: Use Prior Knowledge and Experience to Make Inferences

An **inference** is an educated guess that you make based on details in a text. In addition to what the author tells you, you can also **use your own prior knowledge and experience** to make inferences.

- As you read, watch movies and plays, and observe the world every day, you gather knowledge and experience.
- When you read something new, look for ways in which the characters and situations resemble ones you have seen before.
- Then, apply that knowledge and experience to make inferences about what you are reading.

Example from "The Gift of the Magi":

Detail from the story: "A furnished flat at $8 per week."

Inference: Della and Jim do not have much money. They have to scrimp and save to get by.

DIRECTIONS: *Use the following chart to record information about the characters listed. Then, make three more inferences about each character based on the details from the story. Some examples are shown.*

Details About Della	Inferences I Can Make About Della
1. She hugs Jim every time he comes home.	Della is deeply in love with her husband.
2. _____	_____
3. _____	_____

Details About Jim	Inferences I Can Make About Jim
1. He greatly values his watch, which was handed down to him.	He has strong feelings for his family.
2. _____	_____
3. _____	_____

Name _____ Date _____

Word List

instigates	depreciate	discreet

A. DIRECTIONS: *Replace each italicized word or group of words with a word from the Word List. Rewrite the sentence in the space provided.*

1. To hide the worn leather strap, Jim takes a *careful* glance at his watch.

   _____

2. For Della, the approaching Christmas holiday *stirs up* a desire to give Jim a special gift.

   _____

3. The beauty of Della's hair is so great that it would *reduce in value* the queen's jewels.

   _____

B. DIRECTIONS: *Decide whether each of the following statements is true or false, and write **T** or **F** on the line provided. Then, explain your answer.*

1. A person who *instigates* conflict might be called a "problem-solver." _____

   _____

2. After 6 years of hard use, a car will *depreciate* in value. _____

   _____

3. Only a *discreet* person should be trusted with a secret. _____

   _____

C. DIRECTIONS: *For each numbered word, choose the word or phrase that is most nearly the same in meaning.*

____ 1. discreet
   A. tactful   B. separate   C. reckless   D. silent

____ 2. instigates
   A. inquires   B. calms   C. stirs up   D. refutes

____ 3. depreciate
   A. criticize   B. intensify   C. retard   D. reduce in value

Name _____ Date _____

"The Gift of the Magi" by O. Henry
Support for Writing a News Story

For your brief news story, use the following graphic organizer. Jot down some notes that answer the six questions that reporters ask: *Who? What? When? Where? Why? How?*

Questions	Answers
Who?	
What?	
When?	
Where?	
Why?	
How?	

Use the most important, eye-catching details in your notes to write the lead (opening) paragraph of your human-interest news story on the following lines.

_____

_____

_____

_____

_____

_____

_____

On a separate piece of paper, write your revised lead paragraph and choose other details to write the remaining paragraphs of your story.

"The Interlopers" by Saki
Literary Analysis: Irony and Surprise Ending

Irony is a difference or a contradiction between appearance and reality or between what is expected and what actually happens.

- In **situational irony,** something happens in the story that directly contradicts the expectations of a character or the reader. For example, if long-standing enemies suddenly become friends, the situation would be ironic.
- A **surprise ending** often helps to create situational irony through a turn of events that takes the reader by surprise. To make a surprise ending believable, the author builds clues into the story that make the ending logical.

A. DIRECTIONS: *For each of the following excerpts from "The Interlopers," write* **I** *in the space provided if the excerpt is ironic. Write* **N** *if the excerpt is not ironic. On the lines following each item, briefly explain why the excerpt is or is not ironic.*

_____ 1. If only on this wild night, in this dark, lone spot, he might come across Georg Znaeym, man to man, with one to witness—that was the wish that was uppermost in his thoughts. And as he stepped round the trunk of a huge beech he came face to face with the man he sought.

_____

_____

_____ 2. Both had now given up the useless struggle to free themselves from the mass of wood that held them down.

_____

_____

_____ 3. And each prayed a private prayer that his men might be the first to arrive, so that he might be the first to show honorable attention to the enemy that had become a friend.

_____

_____

_____ 4. The two raised their voices in a prolonged hunting call.

_____

_____

B. DIRECTIONS: *On the following lines, briefly explain the surprise ending in "The Interlopers."* *Then, explain how Saki makes the surprise ending seem logical.*

_____

_____

_____

_____

_____

Name _____ Date _____

"The Interlopers" by Saki

Reading: Use Prior Knowledge and Experience to Make Inferences

An **inference** is an educated guess that you make based on details in a text. In addition to what the author tells you, you can also **use your own prior knowledge and experience** to make inferences.

- As you read, watch movies and plays, and observe the world every day, you gather knowledge and experience.
- When you read something new, look for ways in which the characters and situations resemble ones you have seen before.
- Then, apply that knowledge and experience to make inferences about what you are reading.

Example from "The Interlopers":

Detail from the story: "Ulrich von Gradwitz patrolled the dark forest in quest of a human enemy."

Inference: If he finds Georg, Ulrich will try to harm him.

DIRECTIONS: *Use the following chart to record information about the characters listed. Then, make three inferences about each character based on the details from the story. Some examples are shown.*

Details About Ulrich

1. He notices that the roebuck are running in an unusual way.

2. _____

_____

3. _____

_____

Inferences I Can Make About Ulrich

He is keenly observant.

_____

_____

_____

_____

Details About Georg

1. He says he cannot drink wine with an enemy.

2. _____

_____

3. _____

_____

Inferences I Can Make About Georg

He is stubborn and proud.

_____

_____

_____

_____

Unit 2 Resources: Short Stories

"The Interlopers" by Saki
Vocabulary Builder

Word List

precipitous	condolences	languor

A. DIRECTIONS: *Replace each italicized word or group of words with a word from the Word List. Rewrite the sentence in the space provided.*

1. Pinned beneath the huge beech tree, Ulrich experiences pain and *lack of vigor.* _____

   _____

2. Ironically, Georg reassures Ulrich that he will send *expressions of sympathy.* _____

   _____

3. The property in dispute is a narrow strip of *sheer, steeply inclined* woodland. _____

   _____

B. DIRECTIONS: *Revise each sentence so that the underlined vocabulary word is used logically. Be sure to keep the vocabulary word in your revision.*

1. I sent my condolences when I heard that the artist had won a prestigious prize.

   _____

   _____

2. We had an easy half-mile hike over a flat precipitous trail.

   _____

   _____

3. She arises every morning filled with languor and great energy, ready to attack the day.

   _____

   _____

C. DIRECTIONS: *For each numbered word, choose the word or phrase that is most nearly the same in meaning.*

____ 1. condolences
    A. expressions of sympathy   C. shouts of protest
    B. cries of outrage   D. clever replies

____ 2. precipitous
    A. shallow   B. narrow   C. steep   D. rough

____ 3. languor
    A. tardiness   B. weakness   C. gentleness   D. coarseness

"The Interlopers" by Saki
Support for Writing a News Story

To gather information for your brief news story about Ulrich and Georg, use the following graphic organizer. Jot down some notes that answer the six questions that reporters ask: *Who? What? When? Where? Why? How?*

Questions	Answers
Who?	
What?	
When?	
Where?	
Why?	
How?	

Use the most important, eye-catching details in your notes to write the lead (opening) paragraph of your human-interest news story on the following lines.

_____

_____

_____

_____

_____

_____

_____

_____

On a separate piece of paper, write your revised lead paragraph and choose other details to write the remaining paragraphs of your story.

"The Gift of the Magi" by O. Henry

"The Interlopers" by Saki

Build Language Skills: Vocabulary

Word Roots

The Latin root -*mot*- means "to move." This root is contained in the word *motivate*, which means "causing someone or something to move or act," and also in *motive*, which means "the reason that someone or something acts." *Motivation* is the feeling of wanting to move or act.

Example: Ulrich's anger toward Georg motivated him to patrol the forest.

A. DIRECTIONS: *Use a dictionary to look up the origin of each of the following words containing the root -mot-. Write one meaning for each word. Then, write a sentence in which you use the word in a context that makes its meaning clear.*

1. remote   Meaning: _____

    Sentence: _____

2. emotion   Meaning: _____

    Sentence: _____

3. commotion   Meaning: _____

    Sentence: _____

4. promotion   Meaning: _____

    Sentence: _____

Academic Vocabulary Practice

B. DIRECTIONS: *Follow the instructions to write sentences containing the Academic Vocabulary words.*

1. Use *emotion* in a sentence about a newspaper editorial.

    _____

2. Use *motive* in a sentence about a detective thriller.

    _____

3. Use *circumstance* in a sentence about the verdict of a jury at a criminal trial.

    _____

4. Use *categorize* in a sentence about animal species.

    _____

5. Use *aspect* in a sentence about a reaction to a movie.

    _____

Name _____ Date _____

Build Language Skills: Grammar

Irregular Verbs

Unlike regular verbs, the past tense and past participle of **irregular verbs** are not formed by adding *-ed* or *-d* to the present form. Instead, the past tense and past participle are formed in various ways. In some verbs, there is a change of vowels or consonants within the word. Other verbs change both vowels and consonants. Sometimes, the past and the past participle of an irregular verb are identical. In some irregular verbs, though, the past and the past participle have different forms.

Study the forms of the irregular verbs shown in the following chart.

Principal Parts of Irregular Verbs

Present	Present Participle	Past	Past Participle
run	(is) running	ran	(has) run
catch	(is) catching	caught	(has) caught
sit	(is) sitting	sat	(has) sat
fall	(is) falling	fell	(has) fallen
take	(is) taking	took	(has) taken

A. PRACTICE: *On the line provided, write the correct form of the verb in parentheses.*

1. Jim did not know that Della had (selled, sold) her hair.

   _____

2. If you had met Ulrich in the forest, would you have (ran, run) away?

   _____

3. The feud between Ulrich's and Georg's families (began, begun) long ago with a land dispute.

   _____

B. Writing Application: *Read the following sentences and notice the verbs in italics. If the verb is used correctly, write Correct in the space provided. If the verb is not used correctly, rewrite the sentence using the correct form.*

1. Although Saki wrote history, novels, and political satire, he is *knowed* especially for his short stories.

   _____

2. Born in Burma as H. H. Munro, he was *bringed* up in England by two aunts.

   _____

3. As a foreign correspondent, he *spended* time in Poland, Russia, and Paris.

   _____

Name _____ Date _____

"**The Man to Send Rain Clouds**" by Leslie Marmon Silko
"**Old Man of the Temple**" by R. K. Narayan
Literary Analysis: Setting

The **setting** of a story is the time and place in which it occurs.

- The time may include not only the historical period but also a specific year, season, and hour of day.
- Place may involve not only geographical location but also the social, economic, and cultural environment.

The importance of setting varies from story to story.

- Sometimes, the setting simply furnishes a backdrop for the action. In such a story, the setting could change, but the characters, actions, and events would remain the same.
- Alternatively, the setting can shape the characters and events. For example, in a story set within a Native American culture, characters may make specific decisions and choices based on the rituals and expectations of the culture.
- Setting can play an important role in establishing or intensifying the atmosphere or over-all mood in a story.

DIRECTIONS: *As you read these stories, concentrate on the specific details about setting. List some of these details, and then describe why they are important to the story.*

"The Man to Send Rain Clouds"

1. Details of characters' physical surroundings: _____
_____

2. Details that reflect the time in which the story takes place: _____
_____

3. Details that reflect the characters' culture: _____
_____

4. Overall importance of setting in the story: _____
_____

"Old Man of the Temple"

5. Details of characters' physical surroundings: _____
_____

6. Details that reflect the time in which the story takes place: _____
_____

7. Details that reflect the characters' culture: _____
_____

8. Overall importance of setting: _____
_____

Name _____   Date _____

"The Man to Send Rain Clouds" by Leslie Marmon Silko
"Old Man of the Temple" by R. K. Narayan
Vocabulary Builder

Word List

penetrated	perverse	awry	venture

A. DIRECTIONS: *Revise each sentence so that the underlined vocabulary word is used logically. Be sure not to change the vocabulary word.*

1. His determination to break school rules is so <u>perverse</u> that the principal sent him a note of congratulations.

   _____

   _____

2. He was really happy when he discovered that his well-laid plans had gone <u>awry</u>.

   _____

   _____

3. When we saw how promptly they had taken their seats, we were impressed by their <u>venture</u>.

   _____

   _____

4. Her winter jacket is so well lined that the bitingly cold wind <u>penetrated</u> it easily.

   _____

   _____

B. DIRECTIONS: *Write the letter of the word or phrase that is the best antonym (word that means the opposite) for the Word List word.*

___ 1. perverse
   A. beneficial
   B. harmful
   C. useful
   D. ridiculous

___ 2. venture
   A. any action
   B. risky action
   C. safe action
   D. useless action

___ 3. awry
   A. crooked
   B. straight
   C. disastrous
   D. enormous

___ 4. penetrated
   A. went through
   B. did not go through
   C. acted carelessly
   D. carefully prepared

Name _____ Date _____

"The Man to Send Rain Clouds" by Leslie Marmon Silko
"Old Man of the Temple" by R. K. Narayan
Writing to Compare Literary Works

Use this chart to take prewriting notes for your essay comparing and contrasting the way the setting of each story influences the characters and story events.

Points of Comparison/Contrast	"The Man to Send Rain Clouds"	"Old Man of the Temple"
Daily lives of characters		
Cultural values and beliefs		
Effects of setting on characters		

"The Necklace" by Guy de Maupassant
Literary Analysis: Character and Characterization

A **character** is a person, an animal, or even an object who participates in the action and experiences the events of a literary work. Writers communicate what characters are like through **characterization.** There are two main types of characterization:

- **Direct characterization:** The writer tells readers what a character is like.
- **Indirect characterization:** The writer gives readers clues to a character. The writer might show the character's behavior, present the character's words and thoughts, describe the character's physical appearance, or reveal what other characters say or think about the character. Often, when a writer uses indirect characterization, it is up to the reader to draw logical conclusions about the character's personality and motivations.

When she sat down to dinner at her round table with its three-day-old cloth, and watched her husband opposite her lift the lid of the soup tureen and exclaim, delighted: "Ah, a good homemade beef stew! There's nothing better . . ." she would visualize elegant dinners with gleaming silver amid tapestried walls peopled by knights and ladies and exotic birds in a fairy forest.

This passage gives readers a glimpse of the personalities of both Madame and Monsieur Loisel through the characters' thoughts and words.

DIRECTIONS: *On the lines provided, briefly explain how each excerpt from the story helps to characterize one or more of the characters.*

1. She suffered constantly, feeling that all the attributes of a gracious life, every luxury, should rightly have been hers. _____

_____

_____

2. She looked at him, irritated, and said impatiently:
"I haven't a thing to wear. How could I go?" _____

_____

_____

3. "Well, all right, then. I'll give you four hundred francs. But try to get something really nice."

_____

_____

4. Madame Forestier said in a faintly waspish tone: "You could have brought it back a little sooner! I might have needed it." _____

_____

_____

5. Madame Loisel started to tremble. Should she speak to her? Yes, certainly she should. And now that she had paid everything back, why shouldn't she tell her the whole story?

_____

_____

Name _____ Date _____

"The Necklace" by Guy de Maupassant

Reading: Ask Questions to Analyze Cause and Effect

A **cause** is an event, action, or feeling that produces a result. An **effect** is the result produced. As you read, **ask questions to analyze cause and effect.** Examining these relationships helps you follow the logic that moves a story forward. As you read, ask yourself:

- What happened?
- Why did it happen?
- What happens as a result?

A single cause may produce several effects. Effects may, in turn, become causes.

A. DIRECTIONS: *Use the cause-and-effect chart below to keep track of events in "The Necklace."*

Cause	Effect
1. Monsieur Loisel receives an invitation to a reception at the Ministry.	Madame Loisel complains that she has nothing to wear.
2.	
3.	
4.	
5.	
6.	

B. DIRECTIONS: *Is the cause of the catastrophe that overtakes Madame Loisel solely of her own making? Or does the author suggest that she is, to some extent, the product of a vain and materialistic society? Discuss your response on the lines below.*

_____

_____

_____

_____

_____

Name _____ Date _____

"The Necklace" by Guy de Maupassant
Vocabulary Builder

Word List

| rueful | resplendent | disheveled | profoundly |

A. DIRECTIONS: *In each item below, think about the meaning of the italicized word, and then answer the question in a complete sentence.*

1. How would a person with a *disheveled* appearance look? _____
   _____

2. If you were *rueful* about one of your actions, how would you feel? _____
   _____

3. Describe something that might move you *profoundly*, and tell how you would feel. _____
   _____

4. Describe a *resplendent* scene that would impress you. _____
   _____

B. DIRECTIONS: *For each item below, write a single sentence using the words as grouped.*

1. *resplendent* and *profoundly*
   _____

2. *rueful* and *disheveled*
   _____

C. DIRECTIONS: *For each numbered word, choose the word or phrase that is most nearly the same in meaning.*

____ 1. profoundly
   A. slightly   B. carefully   C. deeply   D. unpleasantly

____ 2. disheveled
   A. untidy   B. attractive   C. unimpressive   D. unusual

____ 3. resplendent
   A. dim and gloomy   C. bright and shining
   B. beautiful and memorable   D. sad and needy

____ 4. rueful
   A. forgetful   B. regretful   C. angry   D. embarrassed

"**The Necklace**" by Guy de Maupassant
Support for Writing a Written Presentation

For your written presentation helping Madame and Monsieur Loisel, use the lines below to jot down notes about the issues dividing them. For each issue, make a suggestion on how the characters can resolve their conflict.

Issue 1: _____

_____

My suggestions on how to resolve this issue: _____

_____

_____

Issue 2: _____

_____

My suggestions on how to resolve this issue: _____

_____

_____

Issue 3: _____

_____

My suggestions on how to resolve this issue: _____

_____

_____

Issue 4: _____

_____

My suggestions on how to resolve this issue: _____

_____

_____

Now, use your notes to write your written presentation. Make a special effort not to favor one character over the other. Keep your tone neutral, and revise any language that sounds biased in favor of one of the characters.

"Rules of the Game" by Amy Tan
Literary Analysis: Character and Characterization

A **character** is a person, an animal, or even an object who participates in the action and experiences the events of a literary work. Writers communicate what characters are like through **characterization.** There are two main types of characterization:

- **Direct characterization:** The writer tells readers what a character is like.
- **Indirect characterization:** The writer gives readers clues to a character. The writer might show the character's behavior, present the character's words and thoughts, describe the character's physical appearance, or reveal what other characters say or think about the character. Often when a writer uses indirect characterization, it is up to the reader to draw logical conclusions about the character's personality and motivations.

> The next week I bit back my tongue as we entered the store with the forbidden candies. When my mother finished her shopping, she quietly plucked a small bag of plums from the rack and put it on the counter with the rest of the items.

In this example, we get a glimpse of the characters' personalities through their actions. Meimei's mother rewards her for learning the secret of invisible strength and biting back her tongue.

DIRECTIONS: *On the lines provided, briefly explain how each excerpt from the story helps to characterize one or more of the characters.*

1. My mother imparted her daily truths so she could help my older brothers and me rise above our circumstances.

   _____

   _____

2. When we got home, my mother told Vincent to throw the chess set away. "She not want it. We not want it," she said, tossing her head stiffly to the side with a tight, proud smile.

   _____

   _____

3. At the next tournament, I won again, but it was my mother who wore the triumphant grin. "Lost eight piece this time. Last time was eleven. What I tell you? Better off less!" I was annoyed, but I couldn't say anything.

   _____

   _____

4. My mother would proudly walk with me, visiting many shops, buying very little. "This my daughter Wave-ly Jong," she said to whoever looked her way.

   _____

   _____

"Rules of the Game" by Amy Tan

Reading: Ask Questions to Analyze Cause and Effect

A **cause** is an event, action, or feeling that produces a result. An **effect** is the result produced. As you read, **ask questions to analyze cause and effect.** Examining these relationships helps you follow the logic that moves a story forward. As you read, ask yourself the following questions:

- What happened?
- Why did it happen?
- What happens as a result?

A single cause may produce several effects. For example, a character who is saving to buy a bicycle takes a baby-sitting job with her neighbor's children. This leads to her starting a summer play group and starts her thinking about getting a college degree in early childhood education.

Effects may, in turn, become causes. That same character's successful experiences with young children leads her to volunteer on the pediatric floor of a local hospital.

DIRECTIONS: *Use the cause-and-effect chart below to keep track of events in "Rules of the Game."*

Cause	Effect
1. The Jong family goes to a church Christmas party.	Vincent gets a secondhand chess set.
2. Vincent and Winston play chess a lot.	
3.	
4.	
5.	
6.	
7.	

Name _____ Date _____

"**Rules of the Game**" by Amy Tan
Vocabulary Builder

Word List

| pungent | benevolently | retort | malodorous |

A. DIRECTIONS: *In each item below, think about the meaning of the italicized word, and then answer the question in a complete sentence.*

1. If a dish tastes *pungent*, is it spicy or bland? _____
   _____

2. If you reply to a person with a *retort*, are you speaking sweetly or sharply? _____
   _____

3. You enter a restaurant and notice that the air is *malodorous*. Explain why you would choose to eat there or not. _____
   _____

4. If a classmate looks at you *benevolently*, do you feel happy or frightened? _____
   _____

B. DIRECTIONS: *For each item below, write a single sentence using the words as grouped.*

1. *pungent* and *retort*
   _____
   _____

2. *benevolently* and *malodorous*
   _____
   _____

C. DIRECTIONS: *For each numbered word, choose the word or phrase that is most nearly the same in meaning and write its corresponding letter on the line.*

____ 1. pungent
     A. painful   B. unpleasant   C. sharp-smelling   D. sweet-tasting

____ 2. benevolently
     A. kindly   B. offensively   C. critically   D. maliciously

____ 3. retort
     A. joke   B. reply   C. move   D. surprise

____ 4. malodorous
     A. spiteful   B. ugly   C. filthy   D. stinking

"Rules of the Game" by Amy Tan
Support for Writing a Written Presentation

For your written presentation addressed to Waverly and her mother, use the lines below to jot down notes about the issues dividing Waverly and her mother, Mrs. Jong. For each issue, make a suggestion on how the characters can resolve their conflict.

Issue 1: _____

_____

My suggestions on how to resolve this issue: _____

_____

_____

_____

Issue 2: _____

_____

My suggestions on how to resolve this issue: _____

_____

_____

_____

Issue 3: _____

_____

My suggestions on how to resolve this issue: _____

_____

_____

_____

Issue 4: _____

_____

My suggestions on how to resolve this issue: _____

_____

_____

Now, use your notes to write your presentation. Make a special effort not to favor one character over the other. Keep your tone neutral, and revise any language that sounds biased in favor of one of the characters.

"Rules of the Game" by Amy Tan
"The Necklace" by Guy de Maupassant
Build Language Skills: Vocabulary

Word Roots

The Latin root -ver- comes from *verus*, the Latin word for "truth." English words that contain this root, such as *verify* and *verdict*, have meanings related to "truth" and "true."

Not all words with the letters *v-e-r* indicate the Latin root -ver-. English words with the letters *v-e-r* may be related to the root -verd-, meaning "green," or to the root -vert-, meaning "turn."

A. DIRECTIONS: *Look up the origin of each of the following words. Write its root (-ver-, -verd-, or -vert-) on the line. Then, write a sentence using the word in a context that makes its meaning clear.*

1. verify _____

_____

2. verisimilitude _____

_____

3. subversion _____

_____

4. verdant _____

_____

5. vertical _____

_____

Academic Vocabulary Practice

B. DIRECTIONS: *Answer each question using the italicized Academic Vocabulary word.*

1. How does a flashback affect the *sequence* of events in a story? _____

_____

2. Does the title of an essay often identify the writer's *topic*? _____

_____

3. What are some words you might use to describe a writer's tone—his or her *attitude* toward the subject or the characters in a work? _____

_____

4. How can you *verify* the cause-and-effect relationship of events in a story? _____

_____

5. What does the use of quotation marks around a sentence *imply* about the sentence?

_____

"Rules of the Game" by Amy Tan
"The Necklace" by Guy de Maupassant
Build Language Skills: Grammar

Subject and Predicate

A. DIRECTIONS: *Write the answers to each of the following questions on the lines provided.*

1. What is the *subject* of a sentence?

   _____

   _____

2. Write an original sentence and underline the complete subject.

   _____

   _____

3. What is the *predicate* of a sentence?

   _____

   _____

4. Write an original sentence and underline the complete predicate.

   _____

   _____

5. What general rule applies to the agreement of subjects and verbs? State the rule in your own words on the lines below.

   _____

   _____

B. DIRECTIONS: *Read the following sentences and note the verbs in italics. Then, draw a vertical line in each sentence to separate the subject from the predicate.*

1. The man with the camera *cut* across our neighbor's yard.
2. Imitating Granny, Cathy *told* us a story about Goldilocks.
3. Granddaddy Cain *watched* the circles of the hawk and carefully *aimed* his hammer.
4. You *could hear* the squish of Granddaddy's boots from inside the house.
5. I *reached* home just after dark.
6. A plain man of fifty, the expressman named Thompson *was* already inside the car.
7. This recognition of my poor friend *gratified* me.
8. My health *was* permanently *shattered*.

Name _____ Date _____

Literary Analysis: Dialogue and Dialect

Dialogue is a conversation between or among characters in a literary work. In prose, dialogue is usually set off by quotation marks, and a new paragraph indicates a change in speaker. Writers use dialogue to

- reveal character traits and relationships.
- advance the action of the plot and to develop the conflict.
- add variety, color, and realism to narratives.

To make characters even more vivid and to help establish a story's setting, authors may write dialogue that reflects characters' dialect. **Dialect** is a way of speaking that is common to people of a particular region or group. A dialect's words, pronunciations, and grammar are different from those used in the standard form of a language. In the dialect of the American South, for example, speakers often do not pronounce the *g* at the ends of *-ing* words. Dialect often makes characters' personalities, as well as the setting of a story, more vivid.

A. DIRECTIONS: *On the lines provided, briefly explain what each passage of dialogue from the story reveals about the speakers.*

1. "Now, aunty," Camera said, pointin' the thing straight at her.
   "Your mama and I are not related."

   _____

   _____

2. "So here comes . . . this person . . . with a camera, takin pictures of the man and the minister and the woman. Takin' pictures of the man in his misery about to jump, cause life so bad and people been messin' with him so bad. This person takin' up the whole roll of film practically. But savin a few, of course."

   _____

   _____

3. "You standin in the misses' flower bed," say Granddaddy. "This is our own place."

   _____

B. DIRECTIONS: *On the lines below, rewrite each of the passages in dialect in standard English.*

1. Granny wasn't sayin nuthin.

   _____

2. Me and Cathy were waitin, too, cause Granny always got something to say.

   _____

3. And Granny just stare at the twins till their faces swallow up the eager and they don't even care any more about the man jumpin.

   _____

   _____

"Blues Ain't No Mockin Bird" by Toni Cade Bambara

Reading: Visualize the Action to Analyze Cause and Effect

A **cause** is an event, action, or feeling that produces a result. An **effect** is the result produced. When reading a story, **visualize the action to analyze cause and effect.** Examining these relationships helps you follow the logic that drives the plot of a story.

- Based on details in the text, picture the setting, the characters, and the action.
- Use the details of your mental picture to help you identify the relationships between actions and events.

DIRECTIONS: *Use the lines provided to answer the following questions about cause-and-effect relationships in "Blues Ain't No Mockin Bird."*

1. **A.** Why does Granny tell the children a story about a photographer taking pictures of a man about to jump from a bridge?

   _____

   _____

   B. What is the effect of this story?

   _____

   _____

   _____

2. **A.** Why does the male hawk suddenly appear in the story?

   _____

   _____

   B. What effect does the hawk have on Smilin and Camera?

   _____

   _____

   C. How does Granddaddy Cain react to the hawk's appearance?

   _____

   _____

3. **A.** Why does Granddaddy Cain smash the reporters' camera?

   _____

   _____

   B. What effect does this action have on the reporters?

   _____

   _____

Name _____ Date _____

"**Blues Ain't No Mockin Bird**" by Toni Cade Bambara
Vocabulary Builder

Word List

reckless   formality

A. DIRECTIONS: *In each item below, think about the meaning of the italicized word, and then answer the question.*

1. If your older brother's driving is *reckless*, would you be nervous about riding in a car with him? Explain.

_____

_____

2. If someone treats you with *formality*, would your overall impression be of politeness or rudeness? Explain.

_____

_____

B. DIRECTIONS: *Write an original sentence using each of the words below.*

1. *reckless*

_____

_____

2. *formality*

_____

_____

C. DIRECTIONS: *For each numbered word, choose the word or phrase that is most nearly the same in meaning.*

____ 1. formality
    A. lack of form   C. attention to customs
    B. deep respect   D. rudeness

____ 2. reckless
    A. nervous   C. selfish
    B. careless   D. cautious

"Blues Ain't No Mockin Bird" by Toni Cade Bambara
Support for Writing an Informal Letter

For your informal letter from the point of view of a character in the story other than the narrator, use the lines below to jot down notes under each heading.

Character Writing the Letter: _____

Personality Traits of This Character	Events and Details the Character Observed
_____	_____
_____	_____
_____	_____
_____	_____
_____	_____
_____	_____
_____	_____
_____	_____
_____	_____
_____	_____
_____	_____
_____	_____
_____	_____
_____	_____
_____	_____
_____	_____
_____	_____

Now, use your notes to write your informal letter to a friend or relative. Be sure that the details you include and the language you use are consistent with the personality traits you have listed for your character.

Name _____ Date _____

Literary Analysis: Dialogue and Dialect

Dialogue is a conversation between or among characters in a literary work. In prose, dialogue is usually set off by quotation marks, and a new paragraph indicates a change in speaker. Writers use dialogue to

- reveal character traits and relationships.
- advance the action of the plot and to develop the conflict.
- add variety, color, and realism to narratives.

To make characters even more vivid and to help establish a story's setting, authors may write dialogue that reflects characters' dialect. **Dialect** is a way of speaking that is common to people of a particular region or group. A dialect's words, pronunciations, and grammar are different from those used in the standard form of a language. In the dialect of the American South, for example, speakers often do not pronounce the *g* at the ends of *-ing* words. Dialect often makes characters' personalities, as well as the setting of a story, more vivid.

A. DIRECTIONS: *Briefly explain what each passage of dialogue from the story reveals about the speaker.*

1. "We're all right, now! I reckon we've got the Commodore this time. I judge I've got the stuff here that'll take the tuck out of him."

   _____

   _____

2. "Cap, I'm a-going to chance him once more—just this once; and if we don't fetch him this time, the thing for us to do, is to just throw up the sponge and withdraw from the canvass. That's the way *I* put it up."

   _____

   _____

   _____

B. DIRECTIONS: *Use standard English to rewrite each of the passages in dialect.*

1. "'Man that is born of woman is of few days and far between, as Scriptur' says.'"

   _____

   _____

2. "'Yes'ndeedy, it's awful solemn and cur'us; but we've all got to go, one time or another; they ain't no getting around it.'"

   _____

   _____

Name _____ Date _____

"The Invalid's Story" by Mark Twain
Reading: Visualize the Action to Analyze Cause and Effect

A **cause** is an event, action, or feeling that produces a result. An **effect** is the result produced. When reading a story, **visualize the action to analyze cause and effect.** Examining these relationships helps you follow the logic that drives the plot of a story.

- Based on details in the text, picture the setting, the characters, and the action.
- Use the details of your mental picture to help you identify the relationships between actions and events.

A. DIRECTIONS: *Use the lines provided to answer the following questions about cause-and-effect relationships in "The Invalid's Story."*

1. What is the effect on the narrator of his friend's death?

_____

2. **A.** What causes the narrator to rush out from the eating room to the express car?

_____

   B. What effect, unknown to the narrator at the time, results from confusion about the long white-pine boxes that are to be shipped by train?

_____

3. As the train departs, a stranger places a package of Limburger cheese on one end of the coffin-box. What are the effects of this event?

_____

_____

4. **A.** What causes an evil odor to spread throughout the express car?

_____

   B. What effects does the odor have on the narrator and the expressman?

_____

B. DIRECTIONS: *Which part of the story created the most vivid impression in you? Describe and explain your choice on the lines below.*

_____

_____

_____

_____

_____

_____

Name _____ Date _____

"The Invalid's Story" by Mark Twain

Vocabulary Builder

Word List

prodigious	deleterious	judicious	placidly	desultory

A. DIRECTIONS: *In each item below, think about the meaning of the italicized word, and then answer the question.*

1. Describe someone who is acting *placidly*.
   _____

2. Does weather with *deleterious* effects tend to benefit or harm a building's exterior? Explain.
   _____

3. Would you ask advice from a person with a reputation for offering *judicious* advice? Explain.
   _____

4. How would you feel if you were climbing a *prodigious* mountain?
   _____

5. Would you choose a new computer in a *desultory* way?
   _____

B. DIRECTIONS: *For each item below, write a single sentence using the words as grouped.*

1. *prodigious* and *deleterious*
   _____

2. *judicious* and *placidly*
   _____

3. *desultory* and *deleterious*
   _____

C. DIRECTIONS: *For each numbered word, choose the word or phrase that is most nearly the same in meaning.*

____ 1. prodigious
    A. terrifying   **B.** astonishing   **C.** enormous   **D.** intelligent

____ 2. deleterious
    A. healthful   **B.** beneficial   **C.** damaged   **D.** harmful

____ 3. judicious
    A. foolish   **B.** stern   **C.** wise   **D.** pleasant

"The Invalid's Story" by Mark Twain
Support for Writing an Informal Letter

For your informal letter from Thompson's point of view, use the lines below to jot down notes under each heading.

Personality Traits of Thompson	Events and Details
_____	_____
_____	_____
_____	_____
_____	_____
_____	_____
_____	_____
_____	_____
_____	_____
_____	_____
_____	_____
_____	_____
_____	_____
_____	_____
_____	_____
_____	_____
_____	_____
_____	_____
_____	_____
_____	_____

Now, use your notes to write your informal letter to Thompson's friend or relative. Be sure that the details you include and the language you use are consistent with the personality traits you have listed for Thompson.

"Blues Ain't No Mockin Bird" by Toni Cade Bambara
"The Invalid's Story" by Mark Twain
Build Language Skills: Vocabulary

Word Roots

The Latin root -*sequi*- means "to follow." For example, a *sequence* is "a following of one thing after another." One adjectival form that uses this root is *sequent*, which means "following as a result of" or "effect." Remember that words with this root will be based on the idea of following.

Example: The character gets lost in the mountains and the *sequent* action is frightening.

A. DIRECTIONS: *Use a dictionary to look up the origin of each of the following words. Then, write a sentence using the word in a context that makes its meaning clear.*

1. sequential

_____

2. consecutive

_____

3. persecute

_____

4. consequential

_____

5. non sequitur

_____

Academic Vocabulary Practice

B. DIRECTIONS: *Follow the instructions to write sentences containing the italicized Academic Vocabulary words.*

1. Use *topic* in a sentence about a magazine article.

_____

2. Use *attitude* in a sentence about a character in a literary work.

_____

3. Use *imply* in a sentence about lines from a poem.

_____

4. Use *verify* in a sentence about a scientific experiment.

_____

5. Use *sequence* in a sentence about making or breaking a code.

_____

"Blues Ain't No Mockin Bird" by Toni Cade Bambara
"The Invalid's Story" by Mark Twain
Build Language Skills: Grammar

Active and Passive Voice

A verb in the **active voice** expresses an action done *by* a subject. A verb in the **passive voice** expresses an action done *to* its subject. The passive voice is constructed with a verb phrase consisting of a form of the verb *be* plus a past participle (*are taken, is written, were assigned*).

                                             Direct
                  Subject   Verb   Object
Active voice: <u>Mr. Judson</u> <u>brought</u> boxes of clothes.

                  Subject   Verb Phrase
Passive voice: <u>Boxes</u> of clothes <u>were brought</u> by Mr. Judson.

Notice that a sentence in the passive voice usually contains the word *by:*

The window was broken **by** Kate. The window was fixed **by** Kate's father.

A. DIRECTIONS: *Write A if the verb is in the active voice. Write P if it is in the passive voice.*

_____ 1. Granny noticed the two men in the yard.

_____ 2. One of the men carried a camera.

_____ 3. Granny was irritated by the rude question.

_____ 4. The passengers on the train were suffocated by the smelly cheese.

_____ 5. The conductor's courtesy touched the passengers.

B. DIRECTIONS: *Rewrite each sentence in Exercise A, changing those in the active voice to the passive voice and those in the passive voice to the active voice.*

    Example: The conductor shut the door. <u>The door was shut by the conductor.</u>

1. _____

2. _____

3. _____

4. _____

5. _____

Name _____   Date _____

"The Scarlet Ibis" by James Hurst
"The Golden Kite, the Silver Wind" by Ray Bradbury
Literary Analysis: Symbol and Allegory

A **symbol** is a person, a place, a thing, or an event that represents both itself and a larger idea or feeling. **Symbolism** is the use of symbols in literature. For example, a writer might use a journey as a symbol for the life of a human being.

An **allegory** is a poem or story that has parallel literal and symbolic meanings. On the literal level, the story appears simply as it is told. On the symbolic level, however, every element in the story—including the characters, events, descriptions, and features of the setting—has a symbolic meaning. While an allegory can be understood on the literal level, its full meaning is clear only on the symbolic level. Often, allegories may seem less realistic than nonallegorical works, and they may shed light on current events.

DIRECTIONS: *After you have read the selections, think about which of each work's details and events may be symbolic or allegorical. Then, read these key passages from the stories, and answer the questions that follow.*

"The Scarlet Ibis"

1. That summer, the summer of 1918, was blighted. In May and June there was no rain and the crops withered, curled up, then died under the thirsty sun.

   What is symbolic about the weather in this passage?

   _____

   _____

   _____

2. For a long long time, it seemed forever, I lay there crying, sheltering my fallen scarlet ibis from the heresy of rain.

   How is the symbolism in this passage related to a central theme or insight in the story?

   _____

   _____

   _____

"The Golden Kite, the Silver Wind"

3. And on every night of the year the inhabitants of the Town of the Kite could hear the good clear wind sustaining them. And those in the Town of the Wind could hear the kite singing, whispering, rising, and beautifying them.

   How does this outcome suggest the moral lesson to be drawn from the allegory in this story?

   _____

   _____

   _____

"The Scarlet Ibis" by James Hurst
"The Golden Kite, the Silver Wind" by Ray Bradbury
Vocabulary Builder

Word List

imminent	infallibility	precariously	vile	ravenous	spurn

A. DIRECTIONS: *Revise each sentence so that the underlined vocabulary word is used logically. Be sure not to change the vocabulary word.*

1. A thunderstorm appears to be <u>imminent</u>, so we have decided to stay in the pool.

   _____

2. Josh made so many errors on the math test that we marveled at his <u>infallibility</u>.

   _____

3. A baby spider monkey is dangling <u>precariously</u> from the top of that tall tree, so we are not worried about its safety.

   _____

   _____

4. The crime was so <u>vile</u> that the judge gave the convicted defendant a suspended sentence.

   _____

5. That tiger ate so little meat! It must have been <u>ravenous</u>.

   _____

6. To <u>spurn</u> a fellow guest at a party is a good way to make a new friend.

   _____

B. DIRECTIONS: *Write the letter of the word that is the best antonym of the Word List word.*

___ 1. precariously
   A. dangerously
   B. securely
   C. insecurely
   D. ridiculously

___ 2. vile
   A. disgusting
   B. evil
   C. good
   D. upsetting

___ 3. ravenous
   A. polite
   B. full
   C. nervous
   D. pleasant

___ 4. spurn
   A. welcome
   B. reject
   C. introduce
   D. insult

Name _____ Date _____

"The Scarlet Ibis" by James Hurst
"The Golden Kite, the Silver Wind" by Ray Bradbury
Writing to Compare Literary Works

Use a chart like the one shown to make prewriting notes for your essay comparing and contrasting the use of symbolism in the two stories.

Points of Comparison/Contrast	"The Scarlet Ibis"	"The Golden Kite, the Silver Wind"
Message or lesson expressed in story		
Use of symbols to develop message		
If symbols were omitted, how would the message change?		

Name _____ Date _____

Rebecca Walker
Listening and Viewing

Segment 1: Meet Rebecca Walker
- What early experiences with literature inspired Rebecca Walker to become a writer?
- What is your favorite piece of literature, and why is it important to you? Explain.

_____

_____

_____

_____

Segment 2: Types of Nonfiction
- How can music influence other art forms, especially literature?
- How do you think the emergence of hip-hop has influenced the nonfiction literature that people write today and will write in the future?

_____

_____

_____

_____

Segment 3: The Writing Process
- Which method in Rebecca Walker's writing process would you most likely adopt? Why?

_____

_____

_____

_____

Segment 4: The Rewards of Writing
- What does Rebecca Walker want to convey to young people who read her writing?
- Why do you think it is important for young people to be well-informed about current events?

_____

_____

_____

_____

Learning About Nonfiction

Three important types of nonfiction are essays, articles, and speeches. An **essay** examines and discusses a focused topic, often including the writer's personal viewpoints. In an **article,** a writer gives information about a specific topic, person, or event. In a **speech,** a speaker addresses a topic in front of a live audience. Like essays and articles, speeches may be informative, persuasive, or entertaining.

In nonfiction, just as in fiction, the author's style and tone are important elements. A writer's **style** is the particular way that he or she uses language. Here are some factors that contribute to a writer's distinctive style:

- level of language (formal vs. dialect or slang)
- use of figurative language (simile, metaphor, personification, hyperbole, symbol)
- diction, or word choice
- sentence patterns (long or short, variety in types of sentences, repetition)
- sensory imagery

The **tone** of a work is the author's attitude toward the subject matter, the characters, or the audience of readers or listeners. A work's tone can often be summed up in one word: *playful, solemn, mysterious, ominous, personal,* or *enthusiastic.* Be alert to shifts in tone. Different parts of a single work may deliberately exhibit different tones.

DIRECTIONS: *Circle the letter of the answer that best matches each numbered item.*

1. the style of a letter you write to your local school board
   A. formal   B. chatty   C. slangy

2. the tone of a birthday card you write to your little sister
   A. playful   B. scholarly   C. pessimistic

3. the tone of a speech urging support for a candidate for public office
   A. relaxed   B. persuasive   C. hesitant

4. the style of an essay focusing on one of your childhood experiences
   A. formal   B. informal   C. neutral

5. the tone of an after-dinner speech at an awards ceremony
   A. solemn   B. entertaining   C. poetic

6. the style of a descriptive essay focusing on a field of sunflowers in bloom
   A. sensory   B. persuasive   C. narrative

7. the style of a letter to a childhood friend who now lives in a foreign country
   A. complex   B. remote   C. conversational

8. the tone of an article summarizing the Civil War for high school students
   A. reflective   B. factual   C. humorous

"Before Hip-Hop Was Hip-Hop" by Rebecca Walker
Model Selection: Nonfiction

An **essay** is a brief work of nonfiction that discusses a focused topic and often includes the writer's personal experiences and opinions. An essayist's **style,** or distinctive way of using language, often reflects his or her personality. The **tone** of the essay, or the writer's attitude toward the subject matter and the audience, is also key to understanding an essay.

Essays can be classified by the author's **purpose,** or reason for writing. A **narrative** essay tells a story of actual events or the life experiences of an individual. A **descriptive** essay builds an overall impression of a person, an object, or an experience by using images that appeal to the senses. An **expository** essay provides information, discusses ideas, or explains a process. A **persuasive** essay attempts to convince readers to take a course of action or adopt the writer's viewpoint. A **reflective** essay expresses the writer's thoughts and feelings in response to a personal experience or to an idea.

DIRECTIONS: *Read the following passages from "Before Hip-Hop Was Hip-Hop." In the space provided in the chart, comment briefly on the style, tone, or purpose of each passage.*

Passage from the Essay	Comments on Style, Tone, or Purpose
1. I noted what they wore and how they wore it: the razor sharp creases of their Jordache jeans, the spotless sneakers with the laces left loose and untied.	
2. Intuitively, kids were making a community where there was none; we were affirming our sameness in a world that seemed to only emphasize our difference.	
3. I hope they will marvel at the fact that in the early days of hip-hop, young people were making it up as they went along, following their hearts, following what felt good. I hope they will think about what it takes to create culture that is unique and transcendent and honest, and I hope they will begin to dream about creating a new world for themselves.	

Name _____ Date _____

"A Celebration of Grandfathers" by Rudolfo Anaya
Literary Analysis: Style

An author's **style** is his or her unique way of writing. Style includes every feature of a writer's use of language. Some elements that contribute to an author's style are

- **Diction:** the kinds of words the author uses.
- **Syntax:** the way in which the author arranges words in sentences.
- **Tone:** the author's attitude toward his or her audience or subject.

A writer's diction and syntax might be described as formal or informal, technical or ordinary, sophisticated or down-to-earth. A writer's tone might be described as serious or playful, friendly or distant, sympathetic or scathing.

DIRECTIONS: *Consider the diction and syntax in the italicized passages from "A Celebration of Grandfathers" in the left-hand column. Then write notes or a sentence in the right-hand column to describe the tone produced by these features of Anaya's style.*

Passage	Tone
1. The old ones had looked deep into *the web that connects all animate and inanimate forms of life,* and they recognized the *great design* of the creation.	1. _____ _____ _____
2. Their faith shone in their eyes; it was in the *strength of their grip,* in the *creases time wove into their faces.*	2. _____ _____ _____
3. All this they passed on to the young, *so that a new generation would know what they had known, so the string of life would not be broken.*	3. _____ _____ _____ _____
4. After he had covered my wells with the cool mud from the irrigation ditch, my grandfather calmly said: *"Know where you stand."*	4. _____ _____ _____ _____
5. *He was a man; he died.* Not in his valley, but nevertheless cared for by his sons and daughters and flocks of grandchildren.	5. _____ _____ _____ _____

"A Celebration of Grandfathers" by Rudolfo Anaya
Reading: Generate Prior Questions to Identify Main Idea and Details

The **main idea** is the central message, insight, or opinion in a work of nonfiction. **Supporting details** are the pieces of evidence that a writer uses to prove the main idea. These details can include facts, statistics, quotations, or anecdotes. To **identify the main idea and supporting details** in a work, **generate questions prior to reading.** Before you read, you can ask yourself questions such as

- Why did the author choose this title?
- How might events in the author's life influence his or her attitude toward the subject?

As you read, look for details that answer those questions and point to the main idea.

A. DIRECTIONS: *Answer the following questions to guide your reading of "A Celebration of Grandfathers."*

1. Consider the connotations or associations of the word *celebration* in Rudolfo Anaya's title. What expectations does this title create in you for the content and tone of the essay?

   _____

   _____

2. In the opening paragraph, Anaya uses a greeting in Spanish: "Buenos días le de Dios, abuelo." What does this greeting lead you to expect about the way in which elders were treated in the traditional culture in which Anaya grew up?

   _____

   _____

3. Anaya, who is considered the father of Chicano literature, has called himself "an oral story-teller" who now tells his tales "on the printed page." What does this self-characterization lead you to expect about the structure and content of his essay?

   _____

   _____

B. DIRECTIONS: *In an essay celebrating grandfathers, what kind of main idea might you expect? What sorts of supporting details might you find in such an essay? Support your answer with examples from your own experience or from your reading.*

   _____

   _____

   _____

   _____

   _____

Name _____ Date _____

"A Celebration of Grandfathers" by Rudolfo Anaya
Vocabulary Builder

Word List

| perplexes | absurdity | permeate | anguish |

A. DIRECTIONS: *Revise each sentence so that the underlined vocabulary word is used logically. Be sure not to change the vocabulary word.*

1. After solving the problem brilliantly, she sadly admits how much it still <u>perplexes</u> her.

   _____

2. Because their explanation seemed so logical, we were struck by its <u>absurdity</u>.

   _____

3. The rain managed to <u>permeate</u> even the stoutest foul-weather gear, so our clothes were dry.

   _____

4. What <u>anguish</u> she felt when her doctor told her that her dog was cured.

   _____

B. DIRECTIONS: *For each item below, write a single sentence using the words as grouped.*

1. *perplexes* and *absurdity*

   _____

2. *permeate* and *anguish*

   _____

C. DIRECTIONS: *For each numbered word, choose the word or phrase that is most nearly the same in meaning.*

____ 1. permeate
   A. make safe
   B. flow over
   C. collect in one spot
   D. spread throughout

____ 2. anguish
   A. enormous joy
   B. great suffering
   C. great intelligence
   D. intense fear

____ 3. absurdity
   A. nonsense   B. humor   C. seriousness   D. good judgment

____ 4. perplexes
   A. amuses   B. puzzles   C. frightens   D. challenges

"A Celebration of Grandfathers" by Rudolfo Anaya
Support for Writing Book Jacket Copy

For your book jacket copy, use the lines below to jot down notes under each heading.

Older Person You Admire: _____

Biographical Highlights

_____

_____

_____

_____

_____

_____

Reasons to Admire the Person

_____

_____

_____

_____

_____

_____

_____

Now, use your notes to write copy for your book jacket. Be sure that the details you include will make readers want to know more about your subject.

Name _____ Date _____

Literary Analysis: Style

An author's **style** is his or her unique way of writing. Style includes every feature of a writer's use of language. Some elements that contribute to an author's style are

- **Diction:** the kinds of words the author uses
- **Syntax:** the way in which the author arranges words in sentences
- **Tone:** the author's attitude toward his or her audience or subject

A writer's diction and syntax might be described as formal or informal, technical or ordinary, sophisticated or down-to-earth. A writer's tone might be described as serious or playful, friendly or distant, sympathetic or scathing.

DIRECTIONS: *Consider the diction and syntax in the italicized passages from "On Summer" in the left-hand column below. Then write notes or a sentence in the right-hand column to describe the tone produced by these features of Hansberry's style.*

Passage	Tone
1. The adolescence, admittedly lingering still, brought the traditional passionate commitment to melancholy autumn—*and all that.*	**1.** _____ _____ _____
2. By duration alone, for instance, a summer's day seemed *maddeningly excessive, an utter overstatement.*	**2.** _____ _____ _____
3. And it was also *cool and sweet* to be on the grass and there was usually the scent of freshly cut lemons or melons in the air.	**3.** _____ _____ _____
4. The woman that I met was *as wrinkled as a prune and could hardly hear and barely see and always seemed to be thinking of other times.*	**4.** _____ _____ _____
5. I heard later that she did live to see another summer. *And I have retained my respect for the noblest of the seasons.*	**5.** _____ _____ _____

Name _____ Date _____

"**On Summer**" by Lorraine Hansberry

Reading: Generate Prior Questions to Identify Main Idea and Details

The **main idea** is the central message, insight, or opinion in a work of nonfiction. **Supporting details** are the pieces of evidence that a writer uses to prove the main idea. These details can include facts, statistics, quotations, or anecdotes. To **identify the main idea and supporting details** in a work, **generate questions prior to reading.** Before you read, you can ask yourself questions such as

- Why did the author choose this title?
- How might events in the author's life influence his or her attitude toward the subject?

As you read, look for details that answer those questions and point to the main idea.

A. DIRECTIONS: *Answer the following questions to guide your reading of "On Summer."*

1. The word *on*, meaning "concerning" or "about," has been used in the titles of many essays. What expectations does Hansberry's title create in you, the reader?

   _____

   _____

2. In her first sentence, Hansberry declares, "It has taken me a good number of years to come to any measure of respect for summer." What does this opening sentence lead you to expect about the structure of Hansberry's essay?

   _____

   _____

3. A crucial fact about Hansberry's own life was her struggle against cancer and her premature death from the disease at age thirty-four. How do you think this biographical fact might affect the writer's attitude toward the seasons and the passage of time?

   _____

   _____

B. DIRECTIONS: *In an essay about summer, what kind of main idea might you expect? What sorts of supporting details might you find in such an essay? Support your answer with examples from your own experience or from your reading.*

   _____

   _____

   _____

   _____

Name _____   Date _____

"On Summer" by Lorraine Hansberry
Vocabulary Builder

Word List

| aloofness | melancholy | pretentious | apex |

A. DIRECTIONS: *Revise each sentence so that the underlined vocabulary word is used logically. Be sure not to change the vocabulary word.*

1. Because she mingles easily with her classmates, she has a reputation for <u>aloofness</u>.

_____

2. The team's unexpected victory created intense feelings of <u>melancholy</u> in the stands.

_____

3. Thoroughly <u>pretentious</u>, he always dresses casually and simply.

_____

4. He felt that this failure was surely bound to be the <u>apex</u> of his career.

_____

_____

B. DIRECTIONS: *For each item below, write a single, original sentence using the words as grouped.*

1. *aloofness* and *melancholy*

_____

2. *pretentious* and *apex*

_____

C. DIRECTIONS: *For each numbered word, choose the word or phrase that is most nearly opposite in meaning.*

____ 1. melancholy
   A. upset   B. sadness   C. coldness   D. joy

____ 2. aloofness
   A. unpleasantness   C. courage
   B. friendliness   D. timidity

____ 3. apex
   A. longest distance   C. lowest point
   B. shortest distance   D. most important

____ 4. pretentious
   A. simple   B. realistic   C. unusual   D. elaborate

Name _____ Date _____

Support for Writing Book Jacket Copy

For your book jacket copy, use the chart below to jot down notes under each heading.

Older Person You Admire: _____

Biographical Highlights

_____

_____

_____

_____

_____

_____

_____

Reasons to Admire the Person

_____

_____

_____

_____

_____

_____

_____

Now, use your notes to write copy for your book jacket. Be sure that the details you include will make readers want to know more about your subject.

"A Celebration of Grandfathers" by Rudolfo Anaya
"On Summer" by Lorraine Hansberry
Build Language Skills: Vocabulary

Prefixes

The prefix *con-* or *com-* means "with" or "together." This prefix appears in English words that relate to the ideas of joining or coming together. For example, the word *concurrent* can mean "working *together*" or "happening *along with* something else."

Com- at the beginning of a word is not always a prefix meaning "with" or "together"; sometimes *com-* adds emphasis to the root word.

A. DIRECTIONS: *Use a dictionary to look up the origin of each of the following words. Write one meaning for each word. Then write a sentence using the word in a context that makes its meaning clear.*

1. commensurate _____
   Sentence: _____

2. conduct _____
   Sentence: _____

3. contract _____
   Sentence: _____

4. communal _____
   Sentence: _____

Academic Vocabulary Practice

B. DIRECTIONS: *Answer each question using the italicized Academic Vocabulary word.*

1. Is reading a play *equivalent* to watching a performance of the play? Explain.

   _____

2. What topics or issues might reading a biography of a President encourage you to *contemplate*?

   _____

3. Is an *abstract* of a text longer or shorter than the original?

   _____

4. The author of a short story uses extensive foreshadowing; *hence,* do you have some ideas about the outcome of the plot? Explain.

   _____

5. In an essay on "Friendship," what aspects of the topic would you expect the writer to *illuminate*?

   _____

Name _____ Date _____

Build Language Skills: Grammar

Direct Object and Indirect Object

A **direct object** is the noun or pronoun that receives the action of a verb. You can determine whether a word is a direct object by asking *whom?* or *what?* after an action verb.

> In her essay, Hansberry praises *summer*. [praises *what?*]

> Every morning, Rudolfo greeted his *grandfather*. [greeted *whom?*]

An **indirect object** is a noun or pronoun that names the person or thing that receives the action of the verb. You can tell whether a word is the indirect object by finding the direct object and asking *to / for whom?* or *to / for what?* after the action verb. An indirect object always comes between the subject and the direct object, and it never appears in a sentence without a direct object.

> His grandfather gave *Rudolfo* some wise advice. [*gave advice to whom?*]

A. DIRECTIONS: *Identify each direct object and indirect object in the sentences below by writing the objects on the line provided. After each object, write D.O. for direct object and I.O. for indirect object. Note: Some sentences will have both a direct and an indirect object.*

1. In her essay "On Summer," Lorraine Hansberry tells several anecdotes.

   _____

2. Hansberry's observations offer us a subtle portrait of summer.

   _____

3. Clearly, Rudolfo Anaya greatly admired his grandfather.

   _____

4. Anaya's grandfather offered the younger generation an inspiring model.

   _____

B. Writing Application: *On the lines below, write a paragraph in which you compare and contrast Lorraine Hansberry's "On Summer" with Rudolfo Anaya's "A Celebration of Grandfathers." Use at least two direct objects and two indirect objects in your writing. Underline each direct object once and each indirect object twice.*

   _____

   _____

   _____

   _____

   _____

   _____

Name _____ Date _____

"The News" by Neil Postman
Literary Analysis: Expository Essay

An **expository essay** is a short piece of nonfiction that presents information, discusses ideas, or explains a process. In a good expository essay, the writer provides evidence and examples to present an accurate and complete view of the topic. The writer may also use one or more of the following techniques to provide support, depth, and context.

- **Description:** including language that appeals to the senses
- **Comparison and contrast:** showing similarities and differences among two or more items
- **Cause and effect:** explaining the relationship between events, actions, or situations by showing how one can result in another

DIRECTIONS: *Use the lines provided to answer the questions about Neil Postman's expository essay.*

1. What is the topic that Postman discusses in his essay "The News"?

   _____

2. In paragraphs 7–10, Postman discusses the "structure" of a typical television newscast. Give three specific details that Postman includes in his description of a typical television newscast.

   _____

   _____

   _____

3. How does this description relate to Postman's main idea in the essay?

   _____

   _____

4. Postman compares and contrasts TV news and print media (newspapers and magazines). Briefly summarize three ways in which they are alike or different.

   _____

   _____

   _____

   _____

5. How does this comparison and contrast support the writer's main idea in the essay?

   _____

   _____

6. According to Postman, what underlying cause explains the fact that the national evening news has not expanded from a half-hour format to a full hour?

   _____

   _____

Name _____ Date _____

"The News" by Neil Postman

Reading: Reread to Identify Main Idea and Details

The **main idea** is the central message, insight, or opinion in a work of nonfiction. The **supporting details** in a work help to prove the writer's point. These details can include facts, statistics, quotations, or anecdotes. To help you **identify the main idea and supporting details** in a work, **reread** passages that do not seem to support the work's main idea.

- As you read, note key details to form ideas about what the main idea might be.
- If a detail does not seem to support that main idea, reread the passage to be sure you have not misinterpreted it.
- If necessary, revise your assumptions about the main idea.

DIRECTIONS: *Answer the following questions to guide your reading of "The News."*

1. Reread paragraphs three and four of the essay. Why does Postman describe moving pictures of a burning aircraft carrier as "interesting" and pictures of toppling buildings as "exciting"?

_____

_____

_____

2. According to Postman, why do visual changes on TV have to be more dramatic to be interesting? (Reread the paragraph beginning, "The television screen is smaller than life.")

_____

_____

_____

3. What does Postman mean when he connects television news broadcasts to the "realm of the symbolic"? (Reread the seventh and eighth paragraphs of the essay.)

_____

_____

_____

4. How does the author support his claim that "it is the trivial event that is often best suited for television coverage"? (Reread the long paragraph that begins, "While the form of a news broadcast emphasizes tidiness and control. . . .")

_____

_____

_____

Name _____ Date _____

"The News" by Neil Postman
Vocabulary Builder

Word List

| compensation | temporal | revered | daunting |

A. DIRECTIONS: *Revise each sentence so that the underlined vocabulary word is used logically. Be sure not to change the vocabulary word.*

1. She settled her lawsuit for a substantial amount, refusing all <u>compensation</u> for her injuries.

   _____

2. The climb to the summit seemed <u>daunting</u>, and we thought it would be an easy hike.

   _____

3. Ray is devoted to the <u>temporal</u> realities of his job and is therefore late for work more often than not.

   _____

4. "It is because you are a <u>revered</u> expert," she said, "that we feel free to disregard your opinion."

   _____

B. DIRECTIONS: *Each of the following questions consists of a related pair of words in CAPITAL LETTERS followed by four lettered pairs of words. Choose the pair that best expresses a relationship similar to that expressed in the pair in capital letters.*

1. REVERED : RESPECTED ::
   A. excellent : outstanding
   B. preeminent : unique
   C. peaceful : combative
   D. gaunt : overweight

2. COMPENSATION : INJURY ::
   A. debate : argument
   B. favor : compliment
   C. award : achievement
   D. apology : excuse

3. TIME : TEMPORAL ::
   A. science : scientific
   B. weather : winter
   C. painter : sculptor
   D. illness : sickness

4. INTIMIDATING : DAUNTING : :
   A. neglecting : caring
   B. upsetting : accident
   C. incorrect : erroneous
   D. satirical : sympathetic

Name _____ Date _____

Support for Writing an Announcement Script

For your commercial or public service announcement script, use the chart below to jot down notes under each heading. Include reasons, photos, and a quotation from Postman's essay.

Details to Encourage People to Use a Variety of News Sources	Persuasive Photos an Other Visuals	Direct Quotation and Visual
_____	_____	_____
_____	_____	_____
_____	_____	_____
_____	_____	_____
_____	_____	_____
_____	_____	_____
_____	_____	_____
_____	_____	_____
_____	_____	_____
_____	_____	_____
_____	_____	_____
_____	_____	_____
_____	_____	_____
_____	_____	_____
_____	_____	_____
_____	_____	_____

Now, use your notes to write the script for your announcement. Be sure that the words and visuals all contribute to your goal: persuading people to use a variety of news sources.

"Single Room, Earth View" by Sally Ride
Literary Analysis: Expository Essay

An **expository essay** is a short piece of nonfiction that presents information, discusses ideas, or explains a process. In a good expository essay, the writer provides evidence and examples to present an accurate and complete view of the topic. The writer may also use one or more of the following techniques to provide support, depth, and context.

- **Description:** including language that appeals to the senses
- **Comparison and contrast:** showing similarities and differences among two or more items
- **Cause and effect:** explaining the relationship between events, actions, or situations by showing how one can result in another

DIRECTIONS: *Use the lines provided to answer the questions about Sally Ride's expository essay.*

1. What is the topic that Ride discusses in her essay "Single Room, Earth View"?

   _____

2. How does Ride use comparison and contrast in the second paragraph of the essay, where she discusses airplane travel and spaceflight?

   _____

   _____

   _____

3. How does this discussion relate to Ride's main idea in the essay?

   _____

   _____

4. Give three examples of "civilization's more unfortunate effects on the environment" that Ride describes from space.

   _____

   _____

   _____

5. The space shuttle orbits the Earth once every 90 minutes. Name one effect of that 90-minute orbit.

   _____

   _____

   _____

6. In her conclusion, what does Ride say about comparing airplane travel to spaceflight?

   _____

   _____

Name _____ Date _____

"**Single Room, Earth View**" by Sally Ride
Reading: Reread to Identify Main Idea and Details

The **main idea** is the central message, insight, or opinion in a work of nonfiction. The **supporting details** help to prove the writer's point. These details can include facts, statistics, quotations, or anecdotes. To help you **identify the main idea and supporting details** in a work, **reread** passages that do not seem to support the work's main idea.

- As you read, note key details to form ideas about what the main idea might be.
- If a detail does not seem to support that main idea, reread the passage to be sure you have not misinterpreted it.
- If necessary, revise your assumptions about the main idea.

DIRECTIONS: *Answer the following questions to guide your reading of "Single Room, Earth View."*

1. Reread paragraph three, which begins with "While flying over the Hawaiian Islands." Explain why Ride describes the scene as "surreal" in the last sentence of the paragraph.

   _____

   _____

   _____

2. In paragraph four, why does Ride say that she found it "almost impossible to keep track of where we were at any given moment"?

   _____

   _____

3. Reread paragraph six, in which Ride mentions plate tectonics. Why does she become an instant believer in this scientific theory?

   _____

   _____

   _____

4. What does Ride mean by "the signatures of civilization" in paragraph nine? Reread the paragraph, and then explain the writer's figure of speech.

   _____

   _____

   _____

   _____

Name _____ Date _____

"Single Room, Earth View" by Sally Ride
Vocabulary Builder

Word List

articulate	novice	diffused	extrapolating

A. DIRECTIONS: *Revise each sentence so that the underlined vocabulary word is used logically. Be sure not to change the vocabulary word.*

1. Because he had a reputation as an <u>articulate</u> speaker, we brought along a book to read in case his lecture was boring.

   _____

   _____

2. "We give up!" they cried, after successfully <u>extrapolating</u> a conclusion from the data.

   _____

   _____

3. Because she was a <u>novice</u> player, the organizers hurried to invite her to participate in the tournament.

   _____

   _____

4. The wind had <u>diffused</u> the leaves all over the yard, so we found it easy to gather them into a single pile.

   _____

   _____

B. DIRECTIONS: *Each of the following questions consists of a related pair of words in CAPITAL LETTERS followed by four lettered pairs of words. Choose the pair that best expresses a relationship similar to that expressed in the pair in capital letters.*

1. NOVICE : PROFESSIONAL ::
   A. casual : informal
   B. student : professor
   C. manager : director
   D. athlete : catcher

2. DIFFUSED : SPREAD OUT ::
   A. careful : reckless
   B. anxious : confident
   C. cautious : prudent
   D. unpopular : likeable

3. EXTRAPOLATING : CONCLUSION ::
   A. summary : statistics
   B. creating : writer
   C. scientist : evidence
   D. observing : fact

4. ARTICULATE : INCOMPREHENSIBLE
   A. fierce : savage
   B. tranquil : tempestuous
   C. pretentious : ostentatious
   D. prejudiced : biased

Name _____ Date _____

"**Single Room, Earth View**" by Sally Ride

Support for Writing an Announcement Script

For your commercial or public service announcement script, use the chart below to jot down notes under each heading. Include details that NASA might use to attract new candidates for astronaut training.

Details That Might Appeal to Astronaut Candidates	Persuasive Photos and Other Visuals	Direct Quotation and Visual

Now, use your notes to write the script for your announcement. Be sure that the words and visuals all contribute to your central goal: attracting candidates for astronaut training.

"The News" by Neil Postman
"Single Room, Earth View" by Sally Ride
Build Language Skills: Vocabulary

Prefixes

The prefix *equi-* means "equal." The prefix is contained in the word *equivalent*, which means "equal in meaning." Mathematics uses the prefix *equi-* in the words *equilateral* and *equidistant* as a verbal reinforcement of a mathematical concept.

A. DIRECTIONS: *Use a dictionary to look up the origin of each of the following words. Write one meaning for each word. Then write a sentence using the word in a context that makes its meaning clear.*

1. equity _____

   Sentence: _____

2. equinox _____

   Sentence: _____

3. equilibrium _____

   Sentence: _____

4. equable _____

   Sentence: _____

5. equivocal _____

   Sentence: _____

Academic Vocabulary Practice

B. DIRECTIONS: *Follow the instructions to write sentences containing the Academic Vocabulary words.*

1. Use *equivalent* in a sentence about traveling in a foreign country.

   _____

2. Use *contemplate* in a sentence about the theme of a literary work.

   _____

3. Use *abstract* in a sentence about a magazine article.

   _____

4. Use *hence* in a sentence about a character in a short story.

   _____

5. Use *illuminate* in a sentence about a biography.

   _____

Name _____ Date _____

Build Language Skills: Grammar

A **predicate nominative** is a noun or pronoun that appears with a linking verb. (Linking verbs include *become, grow, look, seem,* and all forms of *be.*) A predicate nominative renames, identifies, or explains the subject of the sentence. In a sentence with a predicate nominative, the linking verb acts as an equal sign between the subject and the predicate nominative. They refer to the same person or thing. In the following examples, the subject is in boldface, the linking verb is in italics, and the predicate nominative is underlined.

Sally Ride *was* the first American <u>woman</u> in space.

This *is* the <u>problem</u> with television news.

A **predicate adjective** is an adjective that appears with a linking verb and describes the subject of the sentence. In the following examples, the subject is in bold type, the linking verb is in italics, and the predicate adjective is underlined.

The **aircraft carrier** *seemed* <u>enormous</u>.

Through the pollutant haze, some **colors** *looked* <u>muted</u>.

A. DIRECTIONS: *In each of the following sentences, circle the linking verb. Then underline each predicate nominative once and each predicate adjective twice.*

1. The television screen is smaller than life.
2. In the cinema the situation is somewhat different.
3. But they are also symbols of a dominant theme of television news.
4. Another severe limitation on television is time.
5. I also became an instant believer in plate tectonics.
6. The Great Wall of China is *not* the only man-made object visible from space.
7. In space, night is very, very black.
8. Part of the fascination with space travel is the element of the unknown.

B. Writing Application: *On the lines below, write a paragraph in which you describe either your favorite natural landscape or your favorite television show. In your paragraph, use at least two predicate nominatives and two predicate adjectives. Underline each predicate nominative once and each predicate adjective twice.*

_____

_____

_____

_____

_____

_____

_____

_____

from **A Lincoln Preface** by Carl Sandburg
"Arthur Ashe Remembered" by John McPhee
Literary Analysis: Biographical Writing

Biographical writing is a form of nonfiction in which a writer tells the life story of another person. Biographies are often written about historical figures. The best biographies do not just list the facts, events, or accomplishments in the subject's life. Although factual information is important, a good biography presents the writer's interpretation of those pieces of information. The biographer shows why an understanding of the subject's life is meaningful to readers.

In biographical writing, the details that an author chooses to describe help create our impression of the subject. Biographers often focus on one or all of the following aspects of a subject's life:

- personality
- relationships
- major life events

- upbringing
- role in important events
- influence on others

DIRECTIONS: *Write your answers to the following questions on the lines provided.*

1. In the excerpt from "A Lincoln Preface," what does the following anecdote reveal about Lincoln's personality?

   "While the war drums beat, he liked best of all the stories told of him, one of two Quakeresses heard talking in a railway car. 'I think that Jefferson will succeed.' 'Why does thee think so?' 'Because Jefferson is a praying man.' 'And so is Abraham a praying man.' 'Yes, but the Lord will think Abraham is joking.'"

   _____
   _____
   _____

2. In a sentence or two, sum up the portrait of Lincoln's personality that Carl Sandburg creates in the excerpt from *A Lincoln Preface*.

   _____
   _____
   _____

3. In "Arthur Ashe Remembered," what are two ways in which John McPhee supports his belief that "When things got tough, [Ashe] had control"?

   _____
   _____
   _____

4. In "Arthur Ashe Remembered," what writing techniques does John McPhee use to give readers a detailed portrait of Arthur Ashe?

   _____
   _____
   _____

from **A Lincoln Preface** by Carl Sandburg
"Arthur Ashe Remembered" by John McPhee
Vocabulary Builder

Word List

| despotic | censure | droll | legacy | enigma | lithe |

A. DIRECTIONS: *Revise each sentence so that the underlined vocabulary word is used logically. Be sure not to change the vocabulary word.*

1. Most of the people enjoy their ruler's use of <u>despotic</u> power.

   _____

2. Mary's personality is an <u>enigma</u>, so we have no difficulty discovering her true motives.

   _____

3. A successful athlete typically has no need of a <u>lithe</u> body.

   _____

4. The movie was so <u>droll</u> that we found ourselves falling asleep in our seats.

   _____

5. In our opinion, the team leader's admirable conduct deserves <u>censure</u>.

   _____

6. The brand-new temple is a <u>legacy</u> from a bygone civilization.

   _____

B. DIRECTIONS: *On the line, write the letter of the choice that is the best synonym for each numbered word.*

___ 1. despotic
  A. temporary
  B. verifiable
  C. tyrannical
  D. true

___ 2. legacy
  A. memento
  B. heirloom
  C. legal document
  D. bracelet

___ 3. lithe
  A. flexible
  B. affluent
  C. devious
  D. permanent

___ 4. enigma
  A. award
  B. joke
  C. advertisement
  D. riddle

Name _____ Date _____

from A Lincoln Preface by Carl Sandburg
"Arthur Ashe Remembered" by John McPhee
Writing to Compare

Use a chart like the one shown to make prewriting notes for an essay comparing your reactions to these two biographical selections.

	from A Lincoln Preface	**"Arthur Ashe Remembered"**
Importance of subject		
My response to each selection		
Main impression author wants to convey		

Unit 3 Resources: Types of Nonfiction
© Pearson Education, Inc., publishing as Pearson Prentice Hall. All rights reserved.
125

Name _____ Date _____

"Carry Your Own Skis" by Lian Dolan
Literary Analysis: Persuasive Essay

A **persuasive essay** is a short nonfiction work that tries to persuade a reader to think or act in a particular way. Persuasive essays usually include one or both of the following:

- **Appeals to reason:** logical arguments based on verifiable evidence, such as facts, statistics, or expert testimony
- **Appeals to emotion:** statements intended to affect listeners' feelings about a subject. These statements often include charged language—words with strong positive or negative associations.

DIRECTIONS: *Use the lines provided to answer the questions about Lian Dolan's persuasive essay.*

1. What opinion or course of action is summed up in the title of the essay, "Carry Your Own Skis"? State the writer's position in your own words.

   _____

   _____

2. In paragraph 2, Dolan mentions luxuries that were not available in the mid-1960s when she learned to ski—for example, valet parking, condos, clothing that keeps you warm and dry. How do these details about what skiing was like in the 1960s support Dolan's main idea?

   _____

   _____

   _____

3. Reread the following excerpt from the essay:

   The real world is riddled with people who have never learned to carry their own skis—the blame-shifters, the no-RSVPers, the coworkers who never participate in those painful group birthdays except if it's their own. I admit it: I don't really get these people.

   In this passage, what are two words or phrases with strong emotional associations? Are these emotional associations positive or negative? Explain your answer.

   _____

   _____

   _____

4. Does Dolan's use of repetition in the essay appeal primarily to reason or to emotion? Write a brief paragraph analyzing the writer's use of repetition. Support your main idea with specific references to the text.

   _____

   _____

   _____

   _____

   _____

Name _____ Date _____

"Carry Your Own Skis" by Lian Dolan
Reading: Reread to Analyze and Evaluate Persuasive Appeals

Persuasive appeals in an essay are the arguments the author makes to persuade readers or listeners to think or act in a particular way. To **analyze and evaluate persuasive appeals,** identify passages in which the author makes an argument in support of his or her position. Then, **reread** those passages to test the logic and reasoning of the author's arguments. Ask yourself these questions:

- Is the author's argument supported by evidence, or is it based on faulty assumptions?
- Does the author demonstrate clear connections between ideas, or does the author make leaps in logic?

A. DIRECTIONS: *Answer the following questions about Lian Dolan's use of persuasive appeals in "Carry Your Own Skis."*

1. Reread the first three paragraphs of the essay. Why do you think Dolan chose to begin her essay about the importance of responsibility with a description of how and why her mother and aunt took up skiing?

   _____

   _____

   _____

2. According to Dolan, what are two of the consequences of *not* taking responsibility for yourself and your stuff? How does she support her argument?

   _____

   _____

   _____

3. Reread the next-to-last paragraph in the essay, beginning, "Now I have a life that includes a husband, two children, a dog, a house." What analogy (comparison) does Dolan draw in this paragraph? Does this analogy support her case effectively, in your view? Why or why not?

   _____

   _____

   _____

B. DIRECTIONS: *Think of two more persuasive appeals that Dolan might have included to support her main idea in this persuasive essay. The persuasive appeals might be appeals to reason or appeals to emotion. In the space below, list and comment on two persuasive appeals that you think might effectively support Dolan's main idea.*

_____

_____

_____

_____

Unit 3 Resources: Types of Nonfiction

"**Carry Your Own Skis**" by Lian Dolan
Vocabulary Builder

Word List

inevitability	potential	riddled

A. DIRECTIONS: *Match each word in Column A with the correct definition in Column B.*

Column A
___ 1. potential
___ 2. riddled
___ 3. inevitability

Column B
A. quality of being certain to happen
B. possibility
C. affected throughout or in every part

B. DIRECTIONS: *In each item below, think about the meaning of the italicized word and then answer the question.*

1. If you thought that being hit by a hurricane in your area was an *inevitability* in the next twenty-four hours, what would you do?

_____

_____

2. If you feel that Alice has the *potential* to become a fine musician, will you encourage her to take music lessons? Why or why not?

_____

_____

3. If the attic in your house is *riddled* with cobwebs, what will you do?

_____

_____

C. DIRECTIONS: *On the line, write the letter of the choice that is the best synonym for each word.*

___ 1. riddled
A. exposed
B. permeated
C. tainted
D. polished

___ 2. inevitability
A. certainty
B. credibility
C. ambiguity
D. complexity

___ 3. potential
A. possibility
B. desire
C. probability
D. withdrawal

Name _____ Date _____

"Carry Your Own Skis" by Lian Dolan
Support for Writing an Abstract

For your abstract of Lian Dolan's "Carry Your Own Skis," use the chart below to jot down notes under each heading.

Topic: _____

_____

Main Idea: _____

_____

Supporting Details:

1. _____

_____

_____

2. _____

_____

_____

3. _____

_____

_____

4. _____

_____

_____

Now, use your notes to write your abstract of "Carry Your Own Skis." Give enough information so that someone who has not yet read the essay can get a clear understanding of what the essay is about.

"Libraries Face Sad Chapter" by Pete Hamill

Literary Analysis: Persuasive Essay

A **persuasive essay** is a short nonfiction work that tries to persuade a reader to think or act in a particular way. Persuasive essays usually include one or both of the following:

- **Appeals to reason:** logical arguments based on verifiable evidence, such as facts, statistics, or expert testimony
- **Appeals to emotion:** statements intended to affect listeners' feelings about a subject. These statements often include charged language—words with strong positive or negative associations.

DIRECTIONS: *Answer these questions about Pete Hamill's persuasive essay.*

1. What is Pete Hamill's opinion and suggested course of action in his essay "Libraries Face Sad Chapter"? State the writer's position in your own words.

   _____

   _____

2. Identify two logical arguments Hamill uses to support his case for the importance of libraries and freely circulating books.

   _____

   _____

   _____

   _____

3. Reread the following excerpt from the essay:

   No teacher sent us to those leathery cliffs of books. Reading wasn't an assignment; it was a pleasure. We read for the combined thrills of villainy and heroism, along with the knowledge of the vast world beyond the parish. Living in those other worlds, we could become other people

   In this passage, what are two words or phrases with strong emotional associations? Are these emotional associations positive or negative? Explain your answer.

   _____

   _____

   _____

   _____

4. At the end of his essay on libraries, Hamill stresses a "debt" that must be honored. On the lines below, explain how Hamill conceives of this "debt" and why it does (or does not) constitute an effective conclusion for his persuasive essay.

   _____

   _____

   _____

   _____

Name _____ Date _____

"Libraries Face Sad Chapter" by Pete Hamill

Reading: Reread to Analyze and Evaluate Persuasive Appeals

Persuasive appeals in an essay are the arguments the author makes to persuade readers or listeners to think or act in a particular way. To **analyze and evaluate persuasive appeals,** identify passages in which the author makes an argument in support of his or her position. Then, **reread** those passages to test the logic and reasoning of the author's arguments. Ask yourself these questions:

- Is the author's argument supported by evidence, or is it based on faulty assumptions?
- Does the author demonstrate clear connections between ideas, or does the author make leaps in logic?

A. DIRECTIONS: *Answer the following questions about Pete Hamill's use of persuasive appeals in "Libraries Face Sad Chapter."*

1. Reread the first section of the essay. Why do you think Hamill chose to open this essay with a reminiscence of how he and his friends used libraries in their childhood?

    _____

    _____

    _____

    _____

2. According to Hamill, why are libraries more important than ever in hard times? In the section "Built by Carnegie," what arguments does Hamill use to support this opinion?

    _____

    _____

    _____

    _____

3. Reread the section entitled "Immigrants' Appreciation." In your opinion, does Hamill appeal primarily to reason or to emotion in this section? Use specific references to the text to explain your answer.

    _____

    _____

    _____

    _____

B. DIRECTIONS: *On the lines below, explain how Hamill uses a mixture of idealism and realism to appeal to his audience. Is this combination effective, in your opinion? Why or why not?*

    _____

    _____

    _____

"Libraries Face Sad Chapter" by Pete Hamill
Vocabulary Builder

Word List

curtailed	medium	duration

A. DIRECTIONS: *Match each word in Column A with the correct definition in Column B.*

Column A

___ 1. duration

___ 2. curtailed

___ 3. medium

Column B

A. reduced; cut short

B. means of communication

C. length of time something lasts

B. DIRECTIONS: *Revise each sentence so that the underlined vocabulary word is used logically. Be sure not to change the vocabulary word.*

1. We were extremely upset to find out that the <u>duration</u> of the exam was only half an hour.

_____

_____

2. The championship tennis match was <u>curtailed</u> by rain, leaving the spectators certain about the outcome.

_____

_____

3. Since e-mail is a rapid and cheap <u>medium</u>, its popularity today is hard to explain.

_____

_____

C. DIRECTIONS: *On the line, write the letter of the choice that is the best synonym for each word.*

___ 1. medium

    A. less than average

    B. severe disappointment

    C. means of communicating

    D. unexpected results

___ 2. curtailed

    A. concluded

    B. cut short

    C. resisted

    D. acknowledged

___ 3. duration

    A. length of time

    B. monotony

    C. durability

    D. inhibition

"Libraries Face Sad Chapter" by Pete Hamill
Support for Writing an Abstract

For your abstract of Pete Hamill's "Libraries Face Sad Chapter," use the chart below to jot down notes under each heading.

Topic: _____

Main Idea: _____

_____

Supporting Details:

1. _____

_____

_____

2. _____

_____

_____

3. _____

_____

_____

4. _____

_____

_____

Now, use your notes to write your abstract of "Libraries Face Sad Chapter." Give enough information so that someone who has not yet read the essay can get a clear understanding of what the essay is about.

"Carry Your Own Skis" by Lian Dolan
"Libraries Face Sad Chapter" by Pete Hamill
Build Language Skills: Vocabulary

The Latin prefix *ante-*

The Latin prefix *ante-* means "before" or "prior to." This prefix appears in words that relate to things that precede other things. The prefix of *anticipate* is *anti-* (a variant of the prefix *ante-*), which also means "before" or "prior to." The following chart shows some other words that share the prefix *ante-*. *Antebellum* means "before the war," while *antechamber* is a small room before or in front of a larger room.

A. DIRECTIONS: *Use a dictionary to look up the origin of each of the following items containing the prefix* ante-. *Write one meaning for each word. Then write a sentence using the word in a context that makes its meaning clear.*

1. antedate

   Meaning: _____

   Sentence: _____

2. A.M.

   Meaning: _____

   Sentence: _____

3. anterior

   Meaning: _____

   Sentence: _____

Academic Vocabulary Practice

B. DIRECTIONS: *Answer each question so that the underlined academic vocabulary word is used logically.*

1. How might you <u>anticipate</u> the outcome of a novel or play?

   _____

2. In a literary work, what is an <u>internal</u> conflict?

   _____

3. What do we mean when we say that an English word is <u>derived</u> from Latin?

   _____

4. What are some adjectives you might use to describe the <u>texture</u> of a story?

   _____

5. What might the symbol of a rose <u>signify</u>?

   _____

"Carry Your Own Skis" by Lian Dolan
"Libraries Face Sad Chapter" by Pete Hamill

Build Language Skills: Grammar

Adjectives

An **adjective** is a word used to describe a noun or pronoun or to give a noun or pronoun a more specific meaning. Adjectives modify nouns and pronouns by telling *what kind, which one, how many,* or *how much.* Sometimes a noun, pronoun, or verb may serve as an adjective.

Adjective:	the *typical* lodge (modifies *lodge*)
Noun as Adjective:	a *rope* tow (noun *rope* modifies *tow*)
Pronoun as Adjective:	carried *her* skis (pronoun *her* modifies *skis*)
Verb as Adjective:	children *left* in the lodge (past participle *left* modifies *children*)

A prepositional phrase may function as an adjective: for example, "rows *of picnic tables.*"

A. DIRECTIONS: *Read the following sentences from "Carry Your Own Skis" and "Libraries Face Sad Chapter." Write all the adjectives in each sentence. You can omit the adjectives a, an,* and the, *but do not forget to list any nouns, pronouns, and verbs used as adjectives.*

1. Getting across the icy parking lot and back seemed a small price to pay for the potential of great fun.

   _____

2. Most days, skiing for me was about freezing rain and constantly trying to catch up to my older, faster, more talented siblings.

   _____

3. We passed into that library between two mock-Corinthian columns that gave the building a majestic aura.

   _____

4. Since those ancient nights around prehistoric campfires, we have needed myth. And heroes. And moral tales.

   _____

B. Writing Application: *Write a brief paragraph describing your school or local library. Include specific details. Use at least five adjectives in your writing and underline each one.*

_____

_____

_____

_____

_____

_____

"I Have a Dream" by Martin Luther King, Jr.
Literary Analysis: Persuasive Speech

A **persuasive speech** is a speech that tries to convince listeners to think or act in a certain way. Persuasive speeches may appeal to reason or emotion or both. In order to engage the audience, speakers often include **rhetorical devices,** special patterns of words and ideas that create emphasis and stir emotion in the audience. Common rhetorical devices include the following:

- **Parallelism:** repeating a grammatical structure or arrangement of words to create a sense of rhythm and momentum
- **Restatement:** expressing the same idea in different words to clarify and stress key points
- **Repetition:** expressing different ideas using the same words or images in order to reinforce concepts and unify the speech

DIRECTIONS: *Read each of the following passages from King's "I Have a Dream" speech. On the lines provided, identify the rhetorical device or devices in each passage. (You may find more than one rhetorical device.) Then briefly explain your answer by citing the words and phrases that exemplify the device.*

1. But one hundred years later, we must face the tragic fact that the Negro is still not free. One hundred years later, the life of the Negro is still sadly crippled by the manacles of segregation and the chains of discrimination. One hundred years later, the Negro lives on a lonely island of poverty in the midst of a vast ocean of material prosperity.

   Rhetorical Device(s): _____

   Explanation: _____

   _____

   _____

2. When the architects of our republic wrote the magnificent words of the Constitution and the Declaration of Independence, they were signing a promissory note to which every American was to fall heir. This note was a promise that all men would be guaranteed the unalienable rights of life, liberty, and the pursuit of happiness.

   Rhetorical Device(s): _____

   Explanation: _____

   _____

   _____

3. It is obvious today that America has defaulted on this promissory note insofar as her citizens of color are concerned. Instead of honoring this sacred obligation, America has given the Negro people a bad check; a check which has come back marked "insufficient funds."

   Rhetorical Device(s): _____

   Explanation: _____

   _____

   _____

Name _____ Date _____

Persuasive techniques are devices used to influence the audience in favor of the author's argument. In addition to presenting evidence in a persuasive speech, a speaker may use the following:

- emotionally charged language
- rhetorical devices, such as parallelism, restatement, and repetition

To analyze and evaluate persuasive techniques, **read aloud** to hear the effect. Notice the emotional impact of the sounds of certain words, as well as the rhythm and momentum created by the word patterns that the author uses. Consider both the purpose and effect of these persuasive techniques and evaluate the author's success in using them to make a convincing argument.

DIRECTIONS: *Read the following excerpts from "I Have a Dream." Then, on the lines provided, answer the questions that follow.*

1. Five score years ago, a great American, in whose symbolic shadow we stand, signed the Emancipation Proclamation.

   A. To which "great American" does King allude in this sentence? _____

   B. What place does King refer to in saying "in whose symbolic shadow we stand"?

   _____

   C. What well-known speech in American history does King echo in saying "five score years ago"? _____

2. Now is the time to make real the promises of Democracy.
   Now is the time to rise from the dark and desolate valley of segregation to the sunlit path of racial justice.

   A. How does this passage illustrate parallelism? _____

   _____

   B. What emotionally charged words or phrases does King use in this passage? _____

   _____

3. This sweltering summer of the Negro's legitimate discontent will not pass until there is an invigorating autumn of freedom and equality.

   A. What image dominates this passage? _____

   _____

   B. How does the passage illustrate parallelism? _____

   _____

Name _____ Date _____

"I Have a Dream" by Martin Luther King, Jr.
Vocabulary Builder

Word List

> hallowed   degenerate   creed

A. DIRECTIONS: *Match each word in Column A with the correct definition in Column B.*

Column A

___ 1. degenerate

___ 2. creed

___ 3. hallowed

Column B

A. sacred

B. statement of belief

C. become worse

B. DIRECTIONS: *In each item, think about the meaning of the italicized word and then answer the question.*

1. If you think that a certain place is *hallowed* ground, would you consider it with respect of indifference? Explain.

   _____

2. Why is a *creed* something that most people take seriously?

   _____

3. If the condition of your house were to *degenerate* over the next few years, what might you do?

   _____

C. DIRECTIONS: *On the line, write the letter of the choice that is the best synonym for each word.*

___ 1. degenerate

   A. produce

   B. augment

   C. deteriorate

   D. rehabilitate

___ 2. hallowed

   A. scooped out

   B. eternal

   C. mysterious

   D. sacred

___ 3. creed

   A. screen

   B. belief

   C. oath

   D. testimony

Name _____ Date _____

"I Have a Dream" by Martin Luther King, Jr.
Support for Writing a Proposal

Use the chart below to make prewriting notes for your proposal.

Issues That Concern Students	Possible Speakers and Topics
1. _____ _____ _____	1. _____ _____ _____
2. _____ _____ _____	2. _____ _____ _____
3. _____ _____ _____	3. _____ _____ _____
4. _____ _____ _____	4. _____ _____ _____
5. _____ _____ _____	5. _____ _____ _____

My Choice of Speaker: _____
_____

Why This Speaker Can Inspire Students: _____
_____
_____
_____

Now, use your notes to write your proposal.

"First Inaugural Address" by Franklin Delano Roosevelt
Literary Analysis: Persuasive Speech

A **persuasive speech** is a speech that tries to convince listeners to think or act in a certain way. Persuasive speeches may appeal to reason or emotion or both. In order to engage the audience, speakers often include **rhetorical devices,** special patterns of words and ideas that create emphasis and stir emotion in the audience. Common rhetorical devices include the following:

- **Restatement:** expressing the same idea in different words to clarify and stress key points
- **Repetition:** expressing different ideas using the same words or images in order to rein-force concepts and unify the speech
- **Analogy:** drawing a comparison that shows a similarity between unlike things
- **Parallelism:** repeating a grammatical structure or arrangement of words to create a sense of rhythm and momentum

DIRECTIONS: *Read each of the following passages from Roosevelt's "First Inaugural Address." On the lines provided, identify the rhetorical device or devices in each passage. (You may find more than one rhetorical device.) Then briefly explain your answer by citing the words and phrases that exemplify the device.*

1. Values have shrunken to fantastic levels; taxes have risen; our ability to pay has fallen

   Rhetorical Device(s): _____

   Explanation: _____

   _____

2. Nature still offers her bounty and human efforts have multiplied it. Plenty is at our door-step, but a generous use of it languishes in the very sight of the supply.

   Rhetorical Device(s): _____

   Explanation: _____

   _____

3. The money changers have fled from their high seats in the temple of our civilization. We may now restore that temple to the ancient truths.

   Rhetorical Device(s): _____

   Explanation: _____

   _____

4. In the field of world policy I would dedicate this nation to the policy of the good neighbor—the neighbor who absolutely respects himself and . . . the rights of others.

   Rhetorical Device(s): _____

   Explanation: _____

   _____

Name _____ Date _____

"**First Inaugural Address**" by Franklin Delano Roosevelt
Reading: Analyze Persuasive Techniques

Persuasive techniques are devices used to influence the audience in favor of the author's argument. In addition to presenting evidence in a persuasive speech, a speaker may use the following:

- emotionally charged language
- rhetorical devices, such as parallelism, restatement, and repetition

To analyze and evaluate persuasive techniques, **read aloud** to hear the effect. Notice the emotional impact of the sounds of certain words, as well as the rhythm and momentum created by the word patterns that the author uses. Consider both the purpose and effect of these persuasive techniques and evaluate the author's success in using them to make a convincing argument.

DIRECTIONS: *Read the following excerpts from Roosevelt's "First Inaugural Address." Then, on the lines provided, answer the questions that follow.*

1. Primarily, this is because the rulers of the exchange of mankind's goods have failed through their own stubbornness and their own incompetence, have admitted that failure and abdicated. Practices of the unscrupulous money changers stand indicted in the court of public opinion, rejected by the hearts and minds of men.

   A. How does the passage illustrate parallelism? _____

   _____

   B. What are three examples of emotionally charged language in the passage? Are the emotional associations positive or negative? _____

   _____

2. Small wonder that confidence languishes, for it thrives only on honesty, on honor, on the sacredness of obligations, on faithful protection, on unselfish performance. Without them it cannot live.

   A. How does this passage exemplify parallelism? _____

   _____

   B. How does Roosevelt use restatement in the passage? _____

   _____

3. We face the arduous days that lie before us in the warm courage of national unity; with the clear consciousness of seeking old and precious moral values; with the clean satisfaction that comes from the stern performance of duty by old and young alike.

   A. What are the emotional associations of the adjectives *warm, clear, precious,* and *clean?*

   _____

   B. How would you describe the rhythm of this passage? _____

   _____

Name _____ Date _____

"First Inaugural Address" by Franklin Delano Roosevelt
Vocabulary Builder

Word List

abdicated	evanescent	arduous

A. DIRECTIONS: *Match each word in Column A with the correct definition in Column B.*

Column A

___ 1. abdicated
___ 2. evanescent
___ 3. arduous

Column B

A. temporary
B. gave up formally
C. difficult

B. DIRECTIONS: *Revise each sentence so that the underlined vocabulary word is used logically. Be sure not to change the vocabulary word.*

1. Because the task was so <u>arduous</u>, we completed it with little effort.

   _____

2. Many of the rich and famous have found to their delight that success is <u>evanescent</u>.

   _____

3. The people hoped that the queen's rule would last a lifetime, so it came as a welcome surprise that she <u>abdicated</u> the throne in the second year of her reign.

   _____

   _____

C. DIRECTIONS: *On the line, write the letter of the choice that is the best synonym for each word.*

___ 1. arduous
   A. affectionate
   B. laborious
   C. resentful
   D. rustic

___ 2. evanescent
   A. luminous
   B. superficial
   C. tending to disappear
   D. conscientious

___ 3. abdicated
   A. alternated
   B. attributed
   C. endorsed
   D. renounced

Name _____ Date _____

Support for Writing a Proposal

Use the chart below to make prewriting notes for your proposal.

Issues That Concern Students	Possible Speakers and Topics
1. _____ _____ _____ _____	1. _____ _____ _____ _____
2. _____ _____ _____ _____	2. _____ _____ _____ _____
3. _____ _____ _____ _____	3. _____ _____ _____ _____
4. _____ _____ _____ _____	4. _____ _____ _____ _____
5. _____ _____ _____	5. _____ _____ _____

My Choice of Speaker: _____

_____

Why This Speaker Can Inspire Students: _____

_____

_____

_____

Now use your notes to write your proposal.

"I Have a Dream" by Martin Luther King, Jr.
"First Inaugural Address" by Franklin Delano Roosevelt
Build Language Skills: Vocabulary

Prefixes

The Latin prefix *in-* means "in," "into," or "within." Thus, the adjective *internal* describes something "inside" or "within." The noun *inhabitant* refers to someone who lives in a certain place. The prefix *in-* sometimes appears as *im-*.

Do not confuse this prefix with the prefix *in-* meaning "not" or "without," as in the words *inefficient* and *immoderate*.

A. DIRECTIONS: *Use a dictionary to look up the origin of each of the following words containing the prefix* in- *or* im-. *Write one meaning for each word. Then write a sentence using the word in a context that makes its meaning clear.*

1. imbibe

   Meaning: _____

   Sentence: _____

2. implant

   Meaning: _____

   Sentence: _____

3. indigenous

   Meaning: _____

   Sentence: _____

Academic Vocabulary Practice

B. DIRECTIONS: *Follow the instructions to write sentences containing the academic vocabulary words.*

1. Use *anticipate* in a sentence about foreshadowing in a literary work.

   _____

2. Use *internal* in a sentence about the domestic issues confronting a nation.

   _____

3. Use *derive* in a sentence about life lessons.

   _____

4. Use *texture* in a sentence about an article of clothing.

   _____

5. Use *signify* in a sentence about the posture or gestures of a public speaker.

   _____

"I Have a Dream" by Martin Luther King, Jr.
"First Inaugural Address" by Franklin Delano Roosevelt
Build Language Skills: Grammar

Adverbs

An **adverb** is a word that modifies a verb, an adjective, or another adverb. Adverbs answer the questions *Where? When? In what way?* and *To what extent?* about the words they modify. You can often make descriptions more meaningful by using adverbs. Look at these examples:

Modifying a Verb:	The audience listened to the speech *attentively.* (*Attentively* modifies the verb *listened.*)
Modifying an Adjective:	Dr. King made an *extremely* eloquent speech. (*Extremely* modifies the adjective *eloquent.*)
Modifying an Adverb:	King used language *very* persuasively. (*Very* modifies the adverb *persuasively.*)

A. PRACTICE: *Read the following passages from "I Have a Dream" and "First Inaugural Address." On the lines provided, write the adverb(s) in each sentence and the word that each adverb modifies. Then, in parentheses, tell whether the word modified by each adverb is a verb, an adjective, or another adverb.*

1. We must forever conduct our struggle on the high plane of dignity and discipline.

   _____

2. I say to you today, my friends, that in spite of the difficulties and frustrations of the moment I still have a dream. It is a dream deeply rooted in the American dream.

   _____

3. Nature still offers her bounty and human efforts have multiplied it.

   _____

4. We may now restore that temple to the ancient truths.

   _____

B. Writing Application: *Write a brief paragraph focusing on a national issue that you think is important. Use at least three adverbs in your writing and underline each adverb that you use.*

_____

_____

_____

_____

_____

_____

_____

"The Talk" by Gary Soto
"Go Deep to the Sewer" by Bill Cosby

Literary Analysis: Humorous Essay

A **humorous essay** is a form of nonfiction writing intended to make the reader laugh. Some humorous writing, often described as harsh or biting, ridicules its subjects. Other humorous writing, often described as gentle, treats its subjects with affection even as it makes fun of them.

Humorous writers often includes one or more of the following figures of speech:

- **hyperbole:** intentional (and often outrageous) overstatement, or exaggeration
- **understatement:** the presentation of something in a restrained or subtle manner; the opposite of hyperbole

In addition to these techniques, the comic writer's **diction,** or word choice, may include funny names, slang, or other examples of verbal humor.

Although humorous writing is meant to entertain, it can have other purposes as well. For example, humor can be used to convey a serious message.

DIRECTIONS: *Write your answers to the following questions on the lines provided.*

1. Read this passage from "The Talk" by Gary Soto:

   The eyes stayed small as well, receding into pencil dots on each side of an unshapely nose that cast remarkable shadows when we turned sideways.

   What humorous technique does the passage exemplify? Briefly explain your answer.

   _____
   _____

2. What serious issue concerning childhood and adolescence does "The Talk" raise? How does the writer's tone in the essay help to gain perspective on that issue?

   _____
   _____

3. In your opinion, how much of Bill Cosby's account of childhood games in "Go Deep to the Sewer" is actually true? Explain your answer.

   _____
   _____

4. Playing football or baseball in city traffic would be truly dangerous. What serious issue does the setting in "Go Deep to the Sewer" bring up?

   _____
   _____

5. In your opinion, are Junior, Albert, Shorty, and Jody in "Go Deep to the Sewer" actual people? What is exaggerated about them, and what might be real?

   _____
   _____

Name _____   Date _____

"The Talk" by Gary Soto
"Go Deep to the Sewer" by Bill Cosby
Vocabulary Builder

Word List

| renegade | feisty | lateral | interpretation |

A. DIRECTIONS: *Revise each sentence so that the underlined vocabulary word is used logically. Be sure not to change the vocabulary word.*

1. We worried about the laziness of the <u>feisty</u> dog.

_____

2. The group of <u>renegade</u> fans loyally cheered the home team whenever it scored.

_____

3. Throwing a <u>lateral</u> pass is easy in a narrow, confined space.

_____

4. Her <u>interpretation</u> of the novel is so objective that it includes personal bias as well as prejudice.

_____

B. DIRECTIONS: *On the line, write the letter of the choice that is the best answer for each analogy question.*

___ 1. RENEGADE : DISLOYAL ::
    A. prudent : cautious
    B. honest : deceptive
    C. reckless : dangerous
    D. rude : obnoxious

___ 2. FEISTY : LAZY ::
    A. hostile : unfriendly
    B. nimble : athletic
    C. aggressive : peaceful
    D. talkative : chatty

___ 3. LATERAL : SIDEWAYS ::
    A. back : front
    B. vertical : perpendicular
    C. behind : around
    D. forward : backward

___ 4. INTERPRETATION : ANALYSIS ::
    A. explanation : study
    B. fact : opinion
    C. learning : predicting
    D. guess : examination

"The Talk" by Gary Soto
"Go Deep to the Sewer" by Bill Cosby
Writing to Compare

Use a chart like the one shown to make prewriting notes for your essay analyzing why the authors chose to discuss their subjects in a humorous fashion.

	"The Talk"	**"Go Deep to the Sewer"**
Characters' present challenges		
Characters' future challenges		
Contributing circumstances		
Why author chose to use humor		

Pat Mora
Listening and Viewing

Segment 1: Meet Pat Mora
- According to Pat Mora, why is it important to use one's "home" language when writing?
- What two languages does Mora use when writing? Why?

_____

_____

_____

_____

Segment 2: Poetry
- How does the shape of "Uncoiling" help you visualize the poem?
- How does the poem's shape add to its intensity?

_____

_____

_____

_____

Segment 3: The Writing Process
- What does Pat Mora do when she revises a poem?
- Do you agree with Pat Mora that revising is an important part of the writing process? Why or why not?

_____

_____

_____

_____

Segment 4: The Rewards of Writing
- Pat Mora believes that writing should be viewed as an exploration. What can you gain from using writing as a tool to explore?

_____

_____

_____

_____

Learning About Poetry

Poetry is a literary form that relies on the precise meanings of words, their emotional associations, their sounds, and the rhythms they create. **Figurative language,** or language that is not intended to be interpreted literally, helps poets to express ideas and feelings in a fresh way.

- A **metaphor** compares two apparently unlike things without using the words *like, as, than,* or *resembles:* "My love is a red, red rose."
- A **simile** uses a connecting word to make such comparisons.
- In **personification,** human qualities are given to nonhuman or inanimate things.
- **Imagery** is descriptive language poets use to create word pictures, or **images.** Images appeal to one or more of the five senses: sight, hearing, touch, taste, and smell.

Poets also use various **sound devices** to give their works a musical quality:

- **Rhythm** is the pattern created by the stressed and unstressed syllables of words.
- **Rhyme** is the repetition of identical or similar sounds in stressed syllables of words.
- **Alliteration** is the repetition of the initial consonant sounds of words. **Assonance** is the repetition of vowel sounds in nearby words. **Consonance** is the repetition of consonants within nearby words in which the separating vowels differ.
- **Onomatopoeia** is the use of a word whose sound imitates its meaning, such as *clank, crackle,* and *sputter.*

The following are some major types and forms of poetry.
Narrative poetry tells a story in verse.

- **Ballad:** a relatively brief, songlike narrative about an adventure or a romance
- **Epic:** a long narrative poem about gods or heroes

Dramatic poetry tells a story using a character's own thoughts or statements.
Lyric poetry expresses the feelings of a single speaker, creating a single effect.

- **Haiku:** a poem containing three lines and seventeen syllables and using imagery to convey a single, vivid emotion
- **Sonnet:** a fourteen-line lyric poem with formal patterns of rhyme, rhythm, and line structure

DIRECTIONS: *Circle the letter of the answer that best matches each numbered item.*

1. words not meant literally
   A. figurative language   B. onomatopoeia   C. quatrain
2. sonnet
   A. narrative poem   B. dramatic poem   C. lyric poem
3. pattern of stressed and unstressed syllables
   A. rhythm   B. free verse   C. tercets
4. "their eyes are lasers"
   A. simile   B. metaphor   C. personification
5. "fear of a frightful fiend"
   A. assonance   B. consonance   C. alliteration

The Poetry of Pat Mora
Model Selection: Poetry

Poets use **sound devices**—such as rhyme, rhythm, alliteration, assonance, and onomatopoeia—to create musical, appealing effects with words. Poets also create unexpected insights and perspectives by using words in fresh ways. **Figurative language**—such as simile, metaphor, and personification—goes beyond the literal meanings of words to express ideas and feelings in a fresh way. A poem also becomes vivid and memorable through the use of **imagery,** sensory language that appeals to one or more of the five senses (sight, hearing, smell, taste, and touch).

DIRECTIONS: *Read the passages from "Uncoiling" and "A Voice." Then, answer the questions that follow each passage.*

1. With thorns, she scratches
    on my window, tosses her hair dark with rain . . . ("Uncoiling")

    A. What figure of speech do these lines contain?

    _____

    B. To which sense(s) does the imagery in these lines appeal?

    _____

2. She spews gusts and thunder,
    spooks pale women who scurry to
      lock doors, windows
        when her tumbleweed skirt starts its spin. ("Uncoiling")

    A. Identify one example of alliteration in these lines.

    _____

    B. Identify one example of assonance in the passage.

    _____

3.   In your house that smelled like
   rose powder, you spoke Spanish formal
   as your father, the judge without a courtroom
   in the country he floated to in the dark
   on a flatbed truck. ("A Voice")

    A. Which lines in the passage illustrate the use of simile? (Hint: There are two similes.)

    _____

    B. Explain the metaphor contained in the words "the judge without a courtroom."

    _____

    _____

Poetry Collection: Langston Hughes, William Wordsworth,
Gabriela Mistral, Jean de Sponde

Literary Analysis: Figurative Language

Figurative language is language that is used imaginatively rather than literally. Figurative language includes one or more **figures of speech,** literary devices that make unexpected comparisons or change the usual meanings of words. The following are figures of speech:

- **Simile:** a comparison of two apparently unlike things using *like, as, than,* or *resembles*
- **Metaphor:** a comparison of two apparently unlike things without using *like, as, than,* or *resembles*
- **Personification:** giving human characteristics to a nonhuman subject
- **Paradox:** a statement, an idea, or a situation that seems contradictory but actually expresses a truth

DIRECTIONS: *Read the following passages and then use the lines provided to identify each example of figurative language. Briefly indicate the reason for your answer.*

1. "Does it stink like rotten meat?" ("Dream Deferred")

   _____

   _____

2. "Life is a broken-winged bird / That cannot fly." ("Dreams")

   _____

   _____

3. "Ten thousand saw I at a glance,
   Tossing their heads in sprightly dance." ("I Wandered Lonely as a Cloud")

   _____

   _____

4. "They flash upon that inward eye
   Which is the bliss of solitude." ("I Wandered Lonely as a Cloud")

   _____

   _____

5. "The wind wandering by night
   rocks the wheat.
   Hearing the loving wind,
   I rock my son." ("Meciendo")

   _____

   _____

6. "What becomes more and more secure, the longer
   it is battered by inconstancy . . .?" ("Sonnets on Love XIII")

   _____

   _____

Poetry Collection: Langston Hughes, William Wordsworth,
Gabriela Mistral, Jean de Sponde

Reading: Read Fluently

Reading fluently is reading smoothly and continuously while also comprehending the text and appreciating the writer's artistry. To improve your fluency when reading poetry, **read in sentences.** Use punctuation—periods, commas, colons, semicolons, and dashes—rather than the ends of lines to determine where to pause or stop reading.

DIRECTIONS: *Read the following passages and then answer the questions on the lines provided.*

1. "God, the Father, soundlessly rocks
   his thousands of worlds.
   Feeling His hand in the shadow,
   I rock my son." ("Meciendo")

   At the ends of which lines would you make major pauses in reading? Minor pauses? No pause at all?

   _____

   _____

2. "But if that dead
   sage could return to life, he would find a clear
   demonstration of his idea, which is not
   pure theory after all. That putative spot
   exists in the love I feel for you, my dear." ("Sonnets on Love XIII")

   After which words would you make a minor pause? After which words would you make a major pause?

   _____

   _____

3. "The waves beside them danced; but they
   Outdid the sparkling waves in glee;
   A poet could not but be gay,
   In such a jocund company;
   I gazed—and gazed—but little thought
   What wealth the show to me had brought:" ("I Wandered Lonely as a Cloud")

   After which words at the end of lines should you not make any pause at all?

   _____

   _____

Name _____ Date _____

Poetry Collection: Langston Hughes, William Wordsworth, Gabriela Mistral, Jean de Sponde
Vocabulary Builder

Word List

deferred	pensive

A. DIRECTIONS: *Answer each of the following questions.*

____ 1. Which of the following is the best synonym for *deferred*?

    A. postponed   **B.** analyzed   **C.** replaced   **D.** completed

____ 2. Which of the following most nearly means the opposite of *pensive*?

    A. deliberate   **B.** thoughtless   **C.** envious   **D.** cautious

B. DIRECTIONS: *For each of the following items, think about the meaning of the italicized word and then answer the question.*

1. Would most of the people at a lively party be likely to be in a *pensive* mood? Why or why not?

_____

_____

2. Would you be happy if your salary or the fee for a job you had completed was unexpectedly *deferred*? Why or why not?

_____

_____

C. DIRECTIONS: *On the line, write the letter of the choice that is the best synonym for each word.*

____ 1. deferred

    A. put off
    B. verified
    C. rephrased
    D. explained

____ 2. pensive

    A. speculative
    B. illusory
    C. meditative
    D. skeptical

Name _____ Date _____

Support for Writing a Description of a Scene

DIRECTIONS: *Use the following lines to make prewriting notes for your description of a scene in nature.*

Choice of Scene: _____

_____

Sensory Details:

1. **Sight:** _____

_____

_____

2. **Sound:** _____

_____

3. **Touch:** _____

_____

_____

4. **Smell:** _____

_____

_____

5. **Taste:** _____

_____

_____

Unified Impression: _____

_____

Now, use your notes to write a few paragraphs or a poem describing a scene in nature.

Name _____ Date _____

Poetry Collection: Richard Brautigan, Emily Dickinson, Stanley Kunitz
Literary Analysis: Figurative Language

Figurative language is language that is used imaginatively rather than literally. Figurative language includes one or more **figures of speech,** literary devices that make unexpected comparisons or change the usual meanings of words. The following are figures of speech:

- **Simile:** a comparison of two apparently unlike things using *like, as, than,* or *resembles*
- **Metaphor:** a comparison of two apparently unlike things without using *like, as, than,* or *resembles*
- **Personification:** giving human characteristics to a nonhuman subject
- **Paradox:** a statement, an idea, or a situation that seems contradictory but actually expresses a truth

DIRECTIONS: *Read the following passages and then use the lines provided to identify each example of figurative language. Briefly indicate the reason for your answer. Note that some passages may exemplify more than one figure of speech.*

1. "Where mammals and computers
   live together in mutually
   programming harmony
   like pure water
   touching pure sky" ("All Watched Over by Machines of Loving Grace")

   _____

   _____

2. "I've heard it in the chillest land—
   And on the strangest Sea—
   Yet, never, in Extremity,
   It asked a crumb—of Me." ("'Hope' is the thing with feathers—")

   _____

   _____

3. "The man who sold his lawn to standard oil
   Joked with his neighbors come to watch the show
   While the bulldozers, drunk with gasoline,
   Tested the virtue of the soil
   Under the branchy sky
   By overthrowing first the privet-row. ("The War Against the Trees")

   _____

   _____

4. "Much madness is divinest Sense—
   To a discerning Eye—
   Much Sense—the starkest Madness—" ("Much Madness is divinest Sense")

   _____

   _____

Name _____ Date _____

Reading: Read Fluently

Reading fluently is reading smoothly and continuously while also comprehending the text and appreciating the writer's artistry. To improve your fluency when reading poetry, **read in sentences.** Use punctuation—periods, commas, colons, semicolons, and dashes—rather than the ends of lines to determine where to pause or stop reading.

DIRECTIONS: *Read the following passages and then answer the questions on the lines provided.*

1. "I like to think
   (it has to be!)
   of a cybernetic ecology
   where we are free of our labors
   and joined back to nature,   5
   returned to our mammal
   brothers and sisters,
   and all watched over
   by machines of loving grace." ("All Watched Over by Machines of Loving Grace")

   At the ends of which lines would you make major pauses in reading? Minor pauses? No pauses at all?

   _____

   _____

   _____

2. "All day the hireling engines charged the trees,
   Subverting them by hacking underground
   In grub-dominions, where dark summer's mole
   Rampages through his halls,
   Till a northern seizure shook   5
   Those crowns, forcing the giants to their knees." ("The War Against the Trees")

   After which words would you make a minor pause? After which words would you make no pause at all?

   _____

   _____

   _____

Poetry Collection: Richard Brautigan, Emily Dickinson, Stanley Kunitz
Vocabulary Builder

Word List

| preliminaries   discerning |

A. DIRECTIONS: *Answer each of the following questions.*

___ 1. Which of the following is the best synonym for *discerning*?
    A. differentiating
    B. insightful
    C. despising
    D. prepared

___ 2. Which of the following most nearly means the opposite of *preliminaries*?
    A. consequences
    B. circumstances
    C. details
    D. considerations

B. DIRECTIONS: *In each of the following items, think about the meaning of the italicized word and then answer the question.*

1. Would you want the pilot of an airplane flight to possess a *discerning* eye? Why or why not?
_____

2. Do *preliminaries* take place before, during, or after the main event?
_____

C. DIRECTIONS: *On the line, write the letter of the choice that is the best synonym for each word.*

___ 1. preliminaries
    A. introductory events
    B. numerous repetitions
    C. critical reviews
    D. coveted awards

___ 2. discerning
    A. moody
    B. pragmatic
    C. superficial
    D. observant

Name _____ Date _____

Support for Writing a Description of a Scene

Use the following lines to make prewriting notes for your description of a scene in nature.

Choice of Scene: _____

_____

Sensory Details:

1. **Sight:** _____

_____

_____

2. **Sound:** _____

_____

_____

3. **Touch:** _____

_____

_____

4. **Smell:** _____

_____

_____

5. **Taste:** _____

_____

_____

Unified Impression: _____

_____

Now, use your notes to write a few paragraphs or a poem describing a scene in nature.

Poetry Collections: Langston Hughes, William Wordsworth, Gabriela Mistral, Jean de Sponde; Richard Brautigan, Emily Dickinson, Stanley Kunitz

Build Language Skills: Vocabulary

The Suffix -able

The Latin suffix -able means "like" or "capable of being." For example, *lovable* means "capable of being loved," while *readable* means "able to be read." The word *fashionable* means "like, or in accordance with, fashion."

A. DIRECTIONS: *Use a dictionary to look up the meanings of each of the following words containing the suffix -able. Write one meaning for each word. Then, write a sentence using the word in a context that makes its meaning clear.*

1. seasonable

   Meaning: _____

   Sentence: _____

2. objectionable

   Meaning: _____

   Sentence: _____

3. changeable

   Meaning: _____

   Sentence: _____

Academic Vocabulary Practice

B. DIRECTIONS: *In each of the following items, think about the meaning of the italicized Academic Vocabulary word and then answer the question.*

1. If an interpretation of a poem were supported by *considerable* evidence, would you be inclined to accept it? Explain why or why not.

   _____

2. Why do poets use great *deliberation* in choosing their words? Explain.

   _____

3. If you were doing an oral interpretation of the two Dickinson poems, would you use a *transition* between the poems? Explain.

   _____

4. Would you be likely to remember a poem that made a great *impact* on you? Explain.

   _____

5. What is an appropriate synonym for the main *concept* in an essay?

   _____

Poetry Collections: Langston Hughes, William Wordsworth, Gabriela Mistral, Jean de Sponde; Richard Brautigan, Emily Dickinson, Stanley Kunitz

Build Language Skills: Grammar

Prepositions and Prepositional Phrases

A **preposition** is a word that relates a noun or pronoun that appears with it to another word in the sentence. Although most prepositions, such as *at, by, in,* and *with,* are single words, some prepositions, such as *because of* and *in addition to,* are compound. In the following example from "The War Against the Trees," the prepositions are in italics.

"Ripped *from* the craters much too big *for* hearts

The club-roots bared their amputated coils"

The **object of a preposition** is the noun or pronoun at the end of a prepositional phrase. In the following example, the prepositional phrase is underlined and the object of the preposition is in italics.

Gabriela Mistral wrote many poems <u>about *children*</u>.

A. PRACTICE: *Read the following passages from the poems in these collections. On the lines provided, write each prepositional phrase. Then, circle the object of the preposition.*

1. "'Hope' is the thing with feathers—
   That perches in the soul—"

   _____

2. "Where we are free of our labors
   and joined back to nature . . ."

   _____

3. "That putative spot
   exists in the love I feel for you, my dear."

   _____

B. Writing Application: *Write a brief paragraph in which you describe the way you get to school in the morning. Use at least five prepositional phrases in your writing, and underline each prepositional phrase you use.*

_____

_____

_____

_____

_____

_____

Poetry Collection: Walter Dean Myers; Alfred, Lord Tennyson; May Swenson
Literary Analysis: Sound Devices

Poets use **sound devices** to emphasize the sound relationships among words. These devices include the following:

- **Alliteration:** the repetition of initial consonant sounds in stressed syllables: "*running and ripping*"
- **Consonance:** the repetition of final consonant sounds in stressed syllables with different vowel sounds, as in *bat* and *met*
- **Assonance:** the repetition of similar vowel sounds in stressed syllables that end with different consonant sounds, as in *please* and *steam*
- **Onomatopoeia:** the use of a word whose sound imitates its meaning, as in *hiss* and *buzz*

DIRECTIONS: *Analyze each poem. For each poem, give one or more examples of each of the following sound devices. If a poem does not use a particular sound device, write* None.

Sound Device	"Summer"	"The Eagle"	"Analysis of Baseball"
Alliteration			
Assonance			
Consonance			
Onomatopoeia			

Name _____ Date _____

Poetry Collection: Walter Dean Myers; Alfred, Lord Tennyson; May Swenson
Reading: Read Fluently

Reading fluently is reading smoothly and continuously while also comprehending the text and appreciating the writer's artistry. To avoid being tripped up by the meaning as you read, **use your senses.** To do so, notice language that appeals to the five senses:

- sight
- hearing
- smell
- taste
- touch

Using your senses will help you connect with a poem and appreciate the effects that the poet creates.

DIRECTIONS: *As you read each poem in this collection, note words and phrases that appeal to your senses. On the following chart, write sensory details in the appropriate section. (Copy the words or phrases exactly.) Because an image can appeal to more than one sense, you may enter a word or phrase more than once.*

Senses	"Summer"	"The Eagle"	"Analysis of Baseball"
Sight			
Hearing			
Smell			
Taste			
Touch			

Name _____ Date _____

Vocabulary Builder

Word List

clasps	azure

A. DIRECTIONS: *Answer each of the following questions.*

____ 1. Which of the following is the best synonym for *clasps* as Tennyson uses it in the line "He clasps the crag with crooked hands"?

    A. handles   C. punches

    B. grips   D. connects

____ 2. Which of the following might be described as *azure*?

    A. a tiger   C. the sky

    B. autumn leaves   D. a diamond

B. DIRECTIONS: *For each of the following items, think about the meaning of the italicized word and then answer the question.*

1. Which of the following colors is closest to *azure*: gold, brown, blue-green, or gray? Explain.

_____

_____

2. If you *clasp* someone's hand in greeting or farewell, is your gesture likely to be friendly or hostile? Explain.

_____

_____

C. DIRECTIONS: *On the line, write the letter of the choice that is the best synonym for each numbered word.*

____ 1. azure   ____ 2. clasps

    A. black   A. holds

    B. crystal   B. dashes

    C. opaque   C. slaps

    D. blue   D. slides

Name _____ Date _____

Support for Writing an Editorial

Use the following chart to develop prewriting notes for your editorial that will be related to a poem in this collection.

Title of Poem: _____

Issue or Topic Related to Poem: _____

_____

My Opinion Statement: _____

_____

_____

Supporting Details:

1. _____
2. _____
3. _____
4. _____
5. _____

Opposing Arguments / Counterarguments:

_____

_____

_____

_____

Now, use your notes to write an editorial about the issue you have chosen.

Name _____ Date _____

Poetry Collection: Yusef Komunyakaa, Lewis Carroll, Edgar Allan Poe
Literary Analysis: Sound Devices

Poets use **sound devices** to emphasize the sound relationships among words. These devices include the following:

- **Alliteration:** the repetition of initial consonant sounds in stressed syllables: "_muffled monotone_"
- **Consonance:** the repetition of final consonant sounds in stressed syllables with different vowel sounds, as in _toll_ and _bell_
- **Assonance:** the repetition of similar vowel sounds in stressed syllables that end with different consonant sounds, as in "_mellow wedding bells_"
- **Onomatopoeia:** the use of a word whose sound imitates its meaning, as in _jangle_ and _knells_

DIRECTIONS: _Analyze each poem. For each poem, give one or more examples of each of the following sound devices. If a poem does not use a particular sound device, write_ None.

Sound Device	"Slam, Dunk, & Hook"	"Jabberwocky"	"The Bells"
Alliteration			
Assonance			
Consonance			
Onomatopoeia			

Name _____ Date _____

Reading: Read Fluently

Reading fluently is reading smoothly and continuously while also comprehending the text and appreciating the writer's artistry. To avoid being tripped up by the meaning of words as you read, **use your senses.** To do so, notice language that appeals to the five senses:

- sight
- hearing
- smell
- taste
- touch

Using your senses will help you connect with a poem and appreciate the effects that the poet creates.

DIRECTIONS: *As you read each poem in this collection, note words and phrases that appeal to your senses. On the following chart, write sensory details in the appropriate section. (Copy the words or phrases exactly.) Because an image can appeal to more than one sense, you may enter a word or phrase more than once.*

Senses	"Slam, Dunk, & Hook"	"Jabberwocky"	"The Bells"
Sight			
Hearing			
Smell			
Taste			
Touch			

Poetry Collection: Yusef Komunyakaa, Lewis Carroll, Edgar Allan Poe
Vocabulary Builder

Word List

jibed   voluminously   metaphysical   palpitating

A. DIRECTIONS: *Match each word in Column A with the correct definition in Column B.*

Column A
___ 1. metaphysical
___ 2. palpitating
___ 3. voluminously
___ 4. jibed

Column B
A. fully
B. spiritual
C. changed direction
D. throbbing

B. DIRECTIONS: *Revise each sentence so that the underlined vocabulary word is used logically. Be sure not to change the vocabulary word.*

1. After the wind jibed, it continued to blow from the same direction: southeast.

   _____

2. The palpitating sound of the drums could scarcely be heard.

   _____

3. Since the reference book covered the topic voluminously, we decided to seek better coverage elsewhere.

   _____

4. Her attitude toward composing poetry was so matter-of-fact that it bordered on the metaphysical.

   _____

C. DIRECTIONS: *On the line, write the letter of the choice that is the best synonym for each numbered word.*

___ 1. voluminously
    A. cleverly
    B. fully
    C. predictably
    D. humorously

___ 2. metaphysical
    A. robust
    B. nimble
    C. spiritual
    D. conversational

___ 3. jibed
    A. shifted
    B. scattered
    C. captured
    D. charged

___ 4. palpitating
    A. beating rapidly
    B. postponing
    C. snooping
    D. evading

Poetry Collection: Yusef Komunyakaa, Lewis Carroll, Edgar Allan Poe

Support for Writing an Editorial

Use the following chart to develop prewriting notes for an editorial that will be related to a poem in this collection.

Title of Poem: _____

Issue or Topic Related to Poem: _____

_____

_____

My Opinion Statement: _____

_____

_____

Supporting Details:

1. _____

_____

2. _____

_____

3. _____

_____

4. _____

_____

5. _____

_____

Opposing Arguments / Counterarguments:

_____

_____

_____

_____

Now, use your notes to write an editorial about the issue you have chosen.

Poetry Collections: Walter Dean Myers; Alfred, Lord Tennyson; May Swenson; and
Yusef Komunyakaa, Lewis Carroll, Edgar Allan Poe

Build Language Skills: Vocabulary

The Suffix -tion

The suffix -*tion* means "the act of" or "the state of being." When a word contains -*tion* as a suffix, it is a noun. For example, the verb "deliberate" means "to carefully think through an issue." When the suffix -*tion* is added, the word *deliberation* means "the act of carefully thinking about an issue."

A. DIRECTIONS: *Use a dictionary to look up the meanings of each of the following words containing the suffix -*tion*. Write one meaning for each word. Finally, write a sentence using the word in a context that makes its meaning clear.*

1. aggravation

   Meaning: _____

   Sentence: _____

2. decoration

   Meaning: _____

   Sentence: _____

3. consolation

   Meaning: _____

   Sentence: _____

Academic Vocabulary Practice

B. DIRECTIONS: *Follow the instructions to write sentences containing the Academic Vocabulary words.*

1. Use *considerable* in a sentence about supporting arguments for an opinion in a newspaper editorial.

   _____

2. Use *deliberation* in a sentence about a panel discussion of the works of Lewis Carroll.

   _____

3. Use *transition* in a sentence about an oral interpretation of two poems by the same poet.

   _____

4. Use *impact* in a sentence about the sound device of onomatopoeia.

   _____

5. Use *concept* in a sentence about a work of science fiction.

   _____

Poetry Collections: Walter Dean Myers; Alfred, Lord Tennyson; May Swenson; and Yusef Komunyakaa, Lewis Carroll, Edgar Allan Poe

Build Language Skills: Grammar

Prepositional Phrases as Modifiers

A **prepositional phrase,** such as *on the court* or *of the bells,* is made up of a preposition and a noun or pronoun, called the object of the preposition, with all of its modifiers. Prepositional phrases may function either as adjectives by modifying nouns or pronouns or as adverbs by modifying verbs, adjectives, and adverbs.

When acting as an adjective, a prepositional phrase is called an *adjective phrase.* **Adjective phrases** modify a noun or pronoun by telling *what kind* or *which one.*

Example: We enjoy the sounds *of summer.* (*of summer* modifies the noun *sounds*)

When functioning as an adverb, a prepositional phrase is called an *adverb phrase.* **Adverb phrases** modify a verb, an adjective, or an adverb by telling *where, when, in what way,* or *to what extent.*

Examples: In summer, we enjoy outdoor activities. (*in summer* modifies the verb *enjoy*)

The forest was quiet *before dawn.* (*before dawn* modifies the adjective *quiet*)

A. PRACTICE: *For each of the following sentences, use the space provided to write all the prepositional phrases. Classify each one as an adjective phrase or an adverb phrase. Then, write the word that each phrase modifies.*

1. Basketball is popular with many sports fans.

   _____

2. The game was invented in the late nineteenth century.

   _____

3. The inventor of basketball was a physical education instructor named James Naismith.

   _____

4. Naismith's new game originally involved two teams of nine players.

   _____

B. Writing Application: *Write a brief paragraph describing your favorite sport or game. In your paragraph, use at least two adjective phrases and two adverb phrases. Underline each prepositional phrase and label it as an adjective phrase or adverb phrase.*

_____

_____

_____

_____

_____

Name _____ Date _____

Poetry by Mary Tallmountain, Galway Kinnell, Naomi Shihab Nye

Literary Analysis: Imagery

Imagery is language that appeals to one or more of the senses—sight, hearing, touch, taste, and smell. The use of imagery allows writers to express their ideas with vividness and immediacy. Images create mental pictures for readers and allow them to make connections between their own experiences and the ideas presented in poems. Some images have a universal appeal and appear in many poems, but most are unique to one poem. Here is an example from Naomi Shihab Nye's poem "Daily": "These T-shirts we fold into / perfect white squares." The words *white* and *squares* appeal to our sense of sight: We can see the folded T-shirts. The word *fold* also appeals to our sense of touch: We can feel the action of folding the shirts.

DIRECTIONS: *Tell which senses (there may be more than one) are appealed to in each of the following passages. Then, describe the complete image that each passage creates in your mind.*

1. "A shade of feeling rippled
   The wind-tanned skin." ("There Is No Word for Goodbye")

   _____

   _____

   _____

2. "Ah, nothing, she said,
   watching the river flash." ("There Is No Word for Goodbye")

   _____

   _____

   _____

3. "Among the fat, overripe, icy black blackberries" ("Blackberry Eating")

   _____

   _____

   _____

4. "These tortillas we slice and fry to crisp strips
   This rich egg scrambled in a gray clay bowl" ("Daily")

   _____

   _____

   _____

5. "This table I dust till the scarred wood shines" ("Daily")

   _____

   _____

   _____

Poetry by Mary Tallmountain, Galway Kinnell, Naomi Shihab Nye
Vocabulary Builder

Word List

penalty   unbidden   shriveled   scarred

A. DIRECTIONS: *Revise each sentence so that the underlined vocabulary word is used logically. Be sure not to change the vocabulary word.*

1. "Your record of community service is so impressive that you deserve a <u>penalty</u>," said the judge.

   _____

2. After we received an invitation, we decided to attend the party <u>unbidden</u>.

   _____

3. Because of the fine weather and the good amount of rain, the flowers in our garden look <u>shriveled</u>.

   _____

4. The furniture is so new that it looks <u>scarred</u> and unstable.

   _____

B. DIRECTIONS: *On the line, write the letter of the choice that is the best synonym, or word with a similar meaning, for each numbered word.*

___ 1. scarred
   A. dented
   B. criminal
   C. aggressive
   D. frightful

___ 2. penalty
   A. setback
   B. repetition
   C. sacrifice
   D. punishment

___ 3. shriveled
   A. moist
   B. absolved
   C. wrinkled
   D. magnified

___ 4. unbidden
   A. uninvited
   B. fantastic
   C. inspirational
   D. ghostly

Name _____ Date _____

Poetry by Mary Tallmountain, Galway Kinnell, Naomi Shihab Nye
Support for Writing to Compare

Use a chart like the one shown to make prewriting notes for an essay comparing and contrasting how the poet's use of imagery adds to the meaning of each poem.

"There Is No Word for Goodbye"
Images of Sokoya →
Speaker's feeling for her aunt: _____

_____

_____

_____

_____

"Blackberry Eating"
Images of blackberries →
Poet's ideas about words: _____

_____

_____

_____

_____

"Daily"
Images of objects/tasks →
Speaker's affection for ordinary things: _____

_____

_____

_____

_____

_____

Name _____ Date _____

Poetry Collection: Ernest Lawrence Thayer, William Stafford, and Sandra Cisneros
Literary Analysis: Narrative Poetry

Narrative poetry is verse that tells a story and includes the same literary elements as narrative prose:

- a plot, or sequence of events
- specific settings
- characters who participate in the action

Also like narrative prose, such as a short story, a narrative poem conveys a **mood,** or **atmosphere**—an overall feeling created by the setting, plot, words, and images. For example, a narrative poem's mood can be gloomy, joyous, or mysterious. Poetry's emphasis on precise words and images makes mood a powerful element in a narrative poem.

DIRECTIONS: *As you read "Casey at the Bat," "Fifteen," and "Twister Hits Houston," answer the following questions.*

"Casey at the Bat"

1. What story does this poem tell?

   _____

2. Who are the two most important characters in the poem?

   _____

3. Briefly describe the poem's outcome.

   _____

4. How does Thayer use details of sound to contribute to the poem's setting?

   _____

   _____

"Fifteen"

5. Who is the speaker in this poem, and what occasion does he recall?

   _____

6. What is the principal conflict in "Fifteen"?

   _____

   _____

"Twister Hits Houston"

7. What details create suspense in this narrative poem?

   _____

   _____

8. How would you describe the atmosphere, or mood, at the end of the poem?

   _____

Poetry Collection: Ernest Lawrence Thayer, William Stafford, and Sandra Cisneros
Reading: Paraphrasing

Paraphrasing is restating in your own words what someone else has written or said. A paraphrase retains the essential meaning and ideas of the original but is simpler to read.

Paraphrasing is especially helpful when reading poetry because poems often contain **figurative language,** words and phrases that are used imaginatively rather than literally. To paraphrase lines in a narrative poem, **picture the action:**

- Based on details in the poem, form a mental image of the setting, the characters, and the characters' actions.
- To be sure that your mental picture is accurate, pay close attention to the way that the poet describes elements of the scene.
- Then, use your own words to describe your mental image of the scene and the action taking place in it.

DIRECTIONS: *On the lines provided, paraphrase the following passages from the narrative poems in this collection. Remember that a paraphrase is a restatement in your own words.*

1. And now the leather-covered sphere came hurtling through the air,
   And Casey stood a-watching it in haughty grandeur there.
   Close by the sturdy batsman the ball unheeded sped;
   "That ain't my style," said Casey. "Strike one," the umpire said. ("Casey at the Bat")

   _____

   _____

   _____

2. I admired all that pulsing gleam, the
   shiny flanks, the demure headlights,
   fringed where it lay; I led it gently
   to the road and stood with that
   companion, ready and friendly. I was fifteen. ("Fifteen")

   _____

   _____

   _____

3. Papa who was sitting on his front porch
   when the storm hit
   said the twister ripped
   the big black oak to splinter . . . ("Twister Hits Houston")

   _____

   _____

   _____

Poetry Collection: Ernest Lawrence Thayer, William Stafford, and Sandra Cisneros
Vocabulary Builder

Word List

pallor	writhing	demure

A. DIRECTIONS: *Match each word in Column A with the correct definition in Column B.*

Column A
___ 1. pallor
___ 2. writhing
___ 3. demure

Column B
A. twisting
B. modest
C. paleness

B. DIRECTIONS: *In each of the following items, think about the meaning of the italicized word and then answer the question.*

1. The doctor remarked on the child's *pallor.* What might be the cause of the child's pallor?

_____

2. If people behave in a *demure* fashion, is it likely that others will criticize them for excessive boldness? Explain.

_____

3. Does *writhing* typically indicate a state of contentment? Why or why not?

_____

C. DIRECTIONS: *On the line, write the letter of the choice that is the best synonym for each numbered word.*

___ 1. writhing
    A. contorting
    B. folding
    C. bristling
    D. sliding

___ 2. demure
    A. resentful
    B. hesitant
    C. modest
    D. shameful

___ 3. pallor
    A. odor
    B. paleness
    C. glint
    D. rumble

Poetry Collection: Ernest Lawrence Thayer, William Stafford, and Sandra Cisneros
Support for Writing a Movie Scene

For your movie scene based on "Casey at the Bat," use the following lines to make notes.

Details from "Casey at the Bat"

1. Characters: _____

_____

2. Setting: _____

_____

3. Actions: _____

_____

4. Mood: _____

Mood in Movie's Opening Scene: _____

_____

_____

_____

_____

_____

Details Contributing to Mood: _____

_____

_____

_____

_____

Camera Angles, Lighting, and so on: _____

_____

_____

_____

_____

_____

Name _____ Date _____

Poetry Collection: Edgar Allan Poe, Edwin Muir, and Richard Wilbur
Literary Analysis: Narrative Poetry

Narrative poetry is verse that tells a story and includes the same literary elements as narrative prose:

- a plot, or sequence of events
- specific settings
- characters who participate in the action

Also like narrative prose, such as a short story, a narrative poem conveys a **mood,** or **atmosphere**—an overall feeling created by the setting, plot, words, and images. For example, a narrative poem's mood can be gloomy, joyous, or mysterious. Poetry's emphasis on precise words and images makes mood a powerful element in a narrative poem.

DIRECTIONS: *As you read "The Raven," "The Horses," and "The Writer," answer the following questions.*

"The Raven"

1. Who is the speaker in the poem? What kind of person is this speaker?

_____

2. Briefly describe the poem's setting.

_____

3. What story does the poem tell?

_____

"The Horses"

4. What events does the speaker in the poem recall?

_____

_____

5. Briefly describe the poem's setting.

_____

6. On what emotional note does the poem end?

_____

"The Writer"

7. What two stories are told by the poem's speaker?

_____

_____

8. How would you describe the atmosphere, or overall mood, of the poem?

_____

Poetry Collection: Edgar Allan Poe, Edwin Muir, and Richard Wilbur
Reading: Paraphrasing

Paraphrasing is restating in your own words what someone else has written or said. A paraphrase retains the essential meaning and ideas of the original but is simpler to read.

Paraphrasing is especially helpful when reading poetry because poems often contain **figurative language,** words and phrases that are used imaginatively rather than literally. To paraphrase lines in a narrative poem, **picture the action:**

- Based on details in the poem, form a mental image of the setting, the characters, and the characters' actions.
- To be sure that your mental picture is accurate, pay close attention to the way that the poet describes elements of the scene.
- Then, use your own words to describe your mental image of the scene and the action taking place in it.

DIRECTIONS: *On the lines provided, paraphrase the following passages from the narrative poems in this collection. Remember that a paraphrase is a restatement in your own words.*

1. Eagerly I wished the morrow—vainly I had tried to borrow
   From my books surcease of sorrow—sorrow for the lost Lenore—
   For the rare and radiant maiden whom the angels name Lenore—
       Nameless here for evermore. ("The Raven")

   _____

   _____

   _____

2. Yet they waited,
   Stubborn and shy, as if they had been sent
   By an old command to find our whereabouts
   And that long-lost archaic companionship. ("The Horses")

   _____

   _____

   _____

3. I remember the dazed starling
   Which was trapped in that very room, two years ago;
   How we stole in, lifted a sash

   And retreated, not to affright it; ("The Writer")

   _____

   _____

   _____

Poetry Collection: Edgar Allan Poe, Edwin Muir, and Richard Wilbur
Vocabulary Builder

Word List

| beguiling | respite | archaic |

A. DIRECTIONS: *Match each word in Column A with the correct definition in Column B.*

Column A	Column B
___ 1. beguiling	A. relief
___ 2. respite	B. charming
___ 3. archaic	C. old-fashioned

B. DIRECTIONS: *Revise each sentence so that the underlined vocabulary word is used logically. Be sure not to change the vocabulary word.*

1. We found the play so <u>beguiling</u> that we walked out of the theater after the first 15 minutes.

_____

2. With no <u>respite</u> in sight, the laborers happily concluded their day's work.

_____

3. That computer is now <u>archaic</u>; it is the newest and best on the market.

_____

C. DIRECTIONS: *On the line, write the letter of the choice that is the best synonym for each numbered word.*

___ 1. archaic
   A. seldom used
   B. cunning and intelligent
   C. intricately chiseled
   D. extremely appealing

___ 2. beguiling
   A. appreciating
   B. acknowledging
   C. overlooking
   D. tricking

___ 3. respite
   A. rest
   B. alteration
   C. joke
   D. insult

Name _____ Date _____

Support for Writing a Movie Scene

For your movie scene based on "The Raven," use the following lines to make notes.

Details from "The Raven"

1. Characters: _____
_____

2. Setting: _____
_____

3. Actions: _____
_____

4. Mood: _____

Mood in Movie's Opening Scene: _____
_____
_____
_____
_____

Details Contributing to Mood: _____
_____
_____
_____
_____

Camera Angles, Lighting, and so on: _____
_____
_____
_____
_____
_____

Poetry Collection: Ernest Lawrence Thayer, William Stafford, and Sandra Cisneros
Poetry Collection: Edgar Allan Poe, Edwin Muir, and Richard Wilbur
Build Language Skills: Vocabulary

The Suffix -age

The suffix -age means "the state or quality of" or "result." For example, *tutelage* means "the state of tutoring someone," and *wreckage* means "the result or remnants of a wreck." This suffix can also refer to the place or abode of someone or something. For instance, an *anchorage* is a place where ships can tie up at anchor.

A. DIRECTIONS: *Use a dictionary, if necessary, to look up the meanings of each of the following words containing the suffix -age. Write one meaning for each word. Then, write a sentence using the word in a context that makes its meaning clear.*

1. bondage

   Meaning: _____

   Sentence: _____

2. coverage

   Meaning: _____

   Sentence: _____

3. orphanage

   Meaning: _____

   Sentence: _____

Academic Vocabulary Practice

B. DIRECTIONS: *Answer each question using the relevant vocabulary word.*

1. Why is a knowledge of grammar required for proper *usage* in English?

   _____

   _____

2. Does repetition typically serve to *emphasize* an idea? Explain.

   _____

3. What is one *mechanism* that an author may use to establish atmosphere or mood?

   _____

4. How do writers use vivid details to make a concept or an emotion less *abstract*?

   _____

   _____

5. What specific words make a simile *distinct* from a metaphor?

   _____

Poetry Collection: Ernest Lawrence Thayer, William Stafford, and Sandra Cisneros
Poetry Collection: Edgar Allan Poe, Edwin Muir, and Richard Wilbur
Build Language Skills: Grammar

Appositive Phrases

An **appositive** is a noun or pronoun placed near another noun or pronoun to identify, rename, or explain it. Notice in the following example that the appositive is set off by commas, which indicates that it is not essential to the meaning of the sentence and can be removed.

Example: The author of "The Raven," *Edgar Allan Poe*, was also a noted short-story writer.

In the following example, *Edgar Allan Poe* is not set off by commas because it is needed to complete the meaning of the sentence.

Example: The American writer *Edgar Allan Poe* is often credited for the invention of the modern short story.

When an appositive has its own modifiers, it forms an **appositive phrase.** Appositive phrases are placed next to a noun or pronoun to add information and details.

Example: We enjoyed reading Poe's "The Cask of Amontillado," *a thrilling tale of suspense.*

A. DIRECTIONS: *Underline the appositive phrase in each of the following sentences. Then, write the word or words that each appositive phrase renames.*

1. Hyperbole, a figure of speech involving deliberate exaggeration, appears in a wide variety of literary works.

   _____

2. For instance, Homer, the oral poet credited with composing the *Iliad* and the *Odyssey*, often uses hyperbole to describe the deeds of epic heroes.

   _____

3. Jonathan Swift employs the same device for fantastic effects in *Gulliver's Travels*, his pointed satire on human life and behavior.

   _____

B. Writing Application: *Write a brief paragraph in which you describe an appliance that you often use at home. Use at least three appositive phrases in your writing, and underline each appositive phrase you use.*

_____

_____

_____

_____

_____

_____

_____

Poetry Collection: Robert Frost, Emily Dickinson, and T. S. Eliot
Literary Analysis: Rhyme and Meter

Rhyme is the repetition of sounds at the ends of words. There are several types of rhyme:

- **Exact rhyme:** the repetition of words that end with the same vowel and consonant sounds, as in *end* and *mend*
- **Slant rhyme:** the repetition of words that end with similar sounds but do not rhyme perfectly, as in *end* and *stand*
- **End rhyme:** the rhyming sounds of words at the ends of lines
- **Internal rhyme:** the rhyming of words within a line

A **rhyme scheme** is a regular pattern of end rhymes in a poem or stanza. A rhyme scheme is described by assigning one letter of the alphabet to each rhyming sound. For example, in "Uphill" by Christina Rossetti, the rhyme scheme is *abab*:

Does the road wind uphill all the <u>way</u>?   *a*
   Yes, to the very <u>end</u>.   *b*
Will the day's journey take the whole long <u>day</u>?   *a*
   From morn to night, my <u>friend</u>.   *b*

Meter is the rhythmical pattern in a line of poetry. Meter results from the arrangement of stressed (´) and unstressed (˘) syllables. When you read aloud a line with a regular meter, you can hear the steady, rhythmic pulse of the stressed syllables:

"and maggie discovered a shell that sang"
"Let not Ambition mock their useful toil"

Not all poems include rhyme, a rhyme scheme, or a regular meter. However, poets often use one or more of these techniques to create musical effects and achieve a sense of unity.

DIRECTIONS: *Read this stanza from "Dream Variations," a poem by Langston Hughes. Identify the rhyme scheme and think about how it emphasizes the speaker's meaning. Also think about Hughes's use of meter in these lines. Then, answer the questions on the lines provided.*

To fling my arms wide
In some place of the sun,
To whirl and to dance
Till the white day is done.
5 Then rest at cool evening
Beneath a tall tree
While night comes on gently,
   Dark like me—
That is my dream!

1. What is the rhyme scheme of this stanza?

_____

2. How does the rhyme scheme help to set off the last line in the stanza?

_____

_____

3. Is the meter in these lines regular or irregular? Explain your answer.

_____

_____

Name _____ Date _____

Reading: Paraphrasing

Paraphrasing is restating in your own words what someone else has written or said. A paraphrase should retain the essential meaning and ideas of the original but should be simpler to read. One way to simplify the text that you are paraphrasing is to **break down long sentences.** Divide long sentences into parts and paraphrase those parts.

- If a sentence contains multiple subjects or verbs, see if it can be separated into smaller sentences with a single subject and a single verb.
- If a sentence contains colons, semicolons, or dashes, create separate sentences by treating those punctuation marks as periods.
- If a sentence contains long phrases or long passages in parentheses, turn each phrase or parenthetical passage into a separate sentence.

Poets often write sentences that span several lines to give their poems fluidity. By breaking down long sentences and paraphrasing them, you can enjoy a poem's fluid quality without missing its meaning.

DIRECTIONS: *On the lines provided, paraphrase the following passages from the poems in this collection. Remember that a paraphrase is a restatement in your own words. In your paraphrases, use short sentences with simple structures.*

1. Then took the other, as just as fair,
   And having perhaps the better claim,
   Because it was grassy and wanted wear;
   Though as for that, the passing there
   Had worn them really about the same. ("The Road Not Taken")

   _____

   _____

   _____

2. The Heroism we recite
   Would be a normal thing
   Did not ourselves the Cubits warp
   For fear to be a King—("We never know how high we are")

   _____

   _____

   _____

3. And when the Foreign Office find a Treaty's gone astray,
   Or the Admiralty lose some plans and drawings by the way,
   There may be a scrap of paper in the hall or on the stair—
   But it's useless to investigate—*Macavity's not there!* ("Macavity: The Mystery Cat")

   _____

   _____

   _____

Name _____ Date _____

Vocabulary Builder

Word List

diverged	warp	bafflement	depravity

A. DIRECTIONS: *Match each word in Column A with the correct definition in Column B.*

Column A

___ 1. diverged
___ 2. warp
___ 3. bafflement
___ 4. depravity

Column B

A. twist
B. corruption
C. branched out
D. puzzlement

B. DIRECTIONS: *In each of the following items, think about the meaning of the italicized word and then answer the question.*

1. If you keep experiencing *bafflement* when working on a crossword puzzle, how likely is it that you will complete the puzzle? Explain.

   _____

2. If you suspect that the wood needed for a new table will *warp*, will you buy it? Why or why not?

   _____

3. Would you employ a job applicant known for *depravity*? Why or why not?

   _____

4. If your answer to a math problem *diverges* from your friend's answer, what might you conclude?

   _____

C. DIRECTIONS: *On the line, write the letter of the choice that is the best synonym for each numbered word.*

___ 1. bafflement
   A. self-confidence
   B. restraint
   C. bewilderment
   D. hostility

___ 2. warp
   A. declare
   B. double-check
   C. distort
   D. replace

___ 3. diverged
   A. differed
   B. duplicated
   C. lengthened
   D. measured

___ 4. depravity
   A. deterioration
   B. disappearance
   C. corruption
   D. candor

Name _____ Date _____

Poetry Collection: Robert Frost, Emily Dickinson, and T. S. Eliot
Support for Writing a Poem

Make prewriting notes for your poem by using a chart like the one shown.

Rhyme Scheme:

_____

_____

_____

Topic/Event/Experience/Emotion:

_____

_____

_____

_____

Images/Details/Phrases/Words:

_____

_____

_____

_____

_____

_____

_____

Main Idea/Theme:

_____

_____

_____

_____

Poetry Collection: Robert Frost, E. E. Cummings, and William Shakespeare
Literary Analysis: Rhyme and Meter

Rhyme is the repetition of sounds at the ends of words. There are several types of rhyme:

- **Exact rhyme:** the repetition of words that end with the same vowel and consonant sounds, as in *end* and *mend*
- **Slant rhyme:** the repetition of words that end with similar sounds but do not rhyme perfectly, as in *end* and *stand*
- **End rhyme:** the rhyming sounds of words at the ends of lines
- **Internal rhyme:** the rhyming of words within a line

A **rhyme scheme** is a regular pattern of end rhymes in a poem or stanza. A rhyme scheme is described by assigning one letter of the alphabet to each rhyming sound. For example, in "Uphill" by Christina Rossetti, the rhyme scheme is *abab*:

Does the road wind uphill all the <u>way</u>?	*a*
Yes, to the very <u>end</u>.	*b*
Will the day's journey take the whole long <u>day</u>?	*a*
From morn to night, my <u>friend</u>.	*b*

Meter is the rhythmical pattern in a line of poetry. Meter results from the arrangement of stressed (´) and unstressed (˘) syllables. When you read aloud a line with a regular meter, you can hear the steady, rhythmic pulse of the stressed syllables:

"and maggie discovered a shell that sang"

"Let not Ambition mock their useful toil"

Not all poems include rhyme, a rhyme scheme, or a regular meter. However, poets often use one or more of these techniques to create musical effects and achieve a sense of unity.

DIRECTIONS: *Read this stanza from "The Day-Breakers," a poem by Arna Bontemps. Identify the rhyme scheme and think about how it emphasizes the speaker's meaning. Also, think about the poet's use of meter in these lines. Then, answer the questions on the lines provided.*

The Day-Breakers

   We are not come to wage a strife
with swords upon this hill:
it is not wise to waste the life
against a stubborn will.

5   Yet would we die as some have done:
beating a way for the rising sun.

1. What is the rhyme scheme of this poem?

_____

2. How does the rhyme scheme help to set off the last two line?

_____

3. Is the meter in these lines regular or irregular? Explain your answer.

_____

_____

Poetry Collection: Robert Frost, E. E. Cummings, and William Shakespeare
Reading: Paraphrasing

Paraphrasing is restating in your own words what someone else has written or said. A paraphrase should retain the essential meaning and ideas of the original but should be simpler to read. One way to simplify the text that you are paraphrasing is to **break down long sentences.** Divide long sentences into parts and paraphrase those parts.

- If a sentence contains multiple subjects or verbs, see if it can be separated into smaller sentences with a single subject and a single verb.
- If a sentence contains colons, semicolons, or dashes, create separate sentences by treating those punctuation marks as periods.
- If a sentence contains long phrases or long passages in parentheses, turn each phrase or parenthetical passage into a separate sentence.

Poets often write sentences that span several lines to give their poems fluidity. By breaking down long sentences and paraphrasing them, you can enjoy a poem's fluid quality without missing its meaning.

DIRECTIONS: *On the lines provided, paraphrase the following passages from the poems in this collection. Remember that a paraphrase is a restatement in your own words. In your paraphrases, use short sentences with simple structures.*

1. But if it had to perish twice,
   I think I know enough of hate
   To say that for destruction ice
   Is also great
   And would suffice. ("Fire and Ice")

   _____

   _____

   _____

2. molly befriended a stranded star
   whose rays five languid fingers were ("maggie and milly and molly and may")

   _____

   _____

3. All the world's a stage,
   And all the men and women merely players:
   They have their exits and their entrances;
   And one man in his time plays many parts,
   His acts being seven ages. ("The Seven Ages of Man")

   _____

   _____

   _____

Name _____ Date _____

Poetry Collection: Robert Frost, E. E. Cummings, and William Shakespeare
Vocabulary Builder

Word List

suffice	languid	woeful	treble

A. DIRECTIONS: *Match each word in Column A with the correct definition in Column B.*

Column A

___ 1. suffice
___ 2. languid
___ 3. woeful
___ 4. treble

Column B

A. high-pitched voice
B. weak
C. be enough
D. sorrowful

B. DIRECTIONS: *Revise each sentence so that the underlined vocabulary word is used logically. Be sure not to change the vocabulary word.*

1. The amount of lemonade in that pitcher will <u>suffice</u>, so we will need to make more.

_____

2. Their behavior was extremely <u>languid</u>, and we could not believe the amount of energy they displayed.

_____

3. Since the news he confided was so <u>woeful</u>, we sent him a note of congratulations.

_____

4. The <u>treble</u> sound of the small child's voice boomed and roared.

_____

C. DIRECTIONS: *On the line, write the letter of the choice that is the best synonym for each numbered word.*

___ 1. treble
   A. abundant
   B. sonorous
   C. irritable
   D. high-pitched

___ 2. woeful
   A. miserable
   B. jovial
   C. aggressive
   D. generous

___ 3. languid
   A. talkative
   B. shameful
   C. drooping
   D. reluctant

___ 4. suffice
   A. exceed
   B. be enough
   C. lack
   D. fear

Name _____ Date _____

Poetry Collection: Robert Frost, E. E. Cummings, and William Shakespeare
Support for Writing a Poem

Make prewriting notes for your poem by using a chart like the one shown.

Rhyme Scheme:

_____

_____

_____

Topic/Event/Experience/Emotion:

_____

_____

_____

_____

Images/Details/Phrases/Words:

_____

_____

_____

_____

_____

_____

_____

Main Idea/Theme:

_____

_____

_____

_____

Poetry Collection: Robert Frost, Emily Dickinson, and T. S. Eliot
Poetry Collection: Robert Frost, E. E. Cummings, and William Shakespeare
Build Language Skills: Vocabulary

The Suffixes -ize and -ism

The verbal suffix -ize means "to make." Thus, the word maximize means "to make something as large as possible." The noun suffix -ism indicates an act or a quality. For example, the word capitalism refers to the economic and political system that depends on private capital and profit-making.

A. DIRECTIONS: Use a dictionary, if necessary, to look up the meanings of each of the following words containing the suffixes -ize and -ism. Write one meaning for each word. Then, write a sentence using the word in a context that makes its meaning clear.

1. mechanize

   Meaning: _____

   Sentence: _____

2. miniaturize

   Meaning: _____

   Sentence: _____

3. athleticism

   Meaning: _____

   Sentence: _____

Academic Vocabulary Practice

B. DIRECTIONS: Follow the instructions to write sentences containing the academic vocabulary words.

1. Use emphasize in a sentence about the theme of a poem.

   _____

2. Use usage in a sentence about a writer's use of dialect in a literary work.

   _____

3. Use mechanism in a sentence about a poet's use of rhyme.

   _____

4. Use abstract in a sentence about sensory images in poetry.

   _____

5. Use distinct in a sentence about a poem's speaker.

   _____

Poetry Collection: Robert Frost, Emily Dickinson, and T. S. Eliot
Poetry Collection: Robert Frost, E. E. Cummings, and William Shakespeare
Build Language Skills: Grammar

Infinitives and Infinitive Phrases

An **infinitive** is a verb form preceded by the word *to* that acts as a noun, an adjective, or an adverb. An **infinitive phrase** is an infinitive with its modifiers or complements. Like infinitives, infinitive phrases can function as nouns, adjectives, or adverbs. Unlike a **prepositional phrase** that begins with *to* and ends with a noun or pronoun, an infinitive phrase always ends with a verb.

Infinitive:	The schoolboy liked *to complain*. (acts as a noun, functioning as the direct object of the sentence)
Infinitive Phrase:	During the storm, I was afraid *to go outdoors*. (acts as an adverb by modifying *afraid*)
Prepositional Phrase:	The girls traveled *to the beach*.

A. DIRECTIONS: *On the line provided, write the infinitive phrase in each sentence. Be sure to write the entire infinitive phrase: the infinite with all of its modifiers or complements. Then, identify whether the infinitive phrase functions as a noun, an adjective, or an adverb.*

1. On the beach, the girls found plenty of shells to collect.

   _____

2. May wanted to keep the smooth round stone.

   _____

3. Maggie pointed out that iridescent shells are sometimes hard to find.

   _____

4. Molly was afraid to admit her fear of the little crab.

   _____

5. The beach was an ideal place to enjoy the warm, sunny afternoon.

   _____

B. Writing Application: *Write a brief paragraph describing one of your favorite hobbies. Use at least three infinitive phrases in your writing, and underline each infinitive phrase you use.*

_____

_____

_____

_____

_____

_____

_____

Poetry by Alice Walker, Bashō, Chiyojo, Walt Whitman, William Shakespeare
Literary Analysis: Lyric Poetry

Lyric poetry is poetry with a musical quality that expresses the thoughts and feelings of a single speaker. Unlike a narrative poem, a lyric does not try to tell a complete story. Instead, it describes an emotion or a mood, often by using vivid imagery, or language that appeals to the senses. A lyric poem is relatively short and usually achieves a single, unified effect.

There are a variety of lyric forms that can create different effects:

- A **sonnet** is a fourteen-line poem that is written in iambic pentameter and that rhymes. Two common sonnet types are the Italian, or Petrarchan, and the English, or Shakespearean. The English, or Shakespearean, sonnet consists of three quatrains, or four-line stanzas, and a final rhyming couplet.
- A **haiku** is an unrhymed Japanese verse form arranged into three lines of five, seven, and five syllables. A haiku often uses a striking image from nature to convey a strong emotion.
- A **free verse** poem does not follow a regular pattern. Free verse employs sound and rhythmic devices, such as alliteration and repetition, and may even use rhyme—but not in a regular pattern, as in metered poetry.

DIRECTIONS: *Analyze each poem. On the chart, write the type of lyric in the first column. Then, in the remaining columns, briefly describe the speaker of the poem, identify the speaker's emotion, and quote an example of a striking image or sound device.*

Author	Type of Lyric	Speaker	Emotion	Image/Sound Device
Walker				
Bashō				
Chiyojo				
Whitman				
Shakespeare				

Poetry by Alice Walker, Bashō, Chiyojo, Walt Whitman, William Shakespeare
Vocabulary Builder

Word List

| stout | intermission | woes | wail |

A. DIRECTIONS: *Revise each sentence so that the underlined vocabulary word is used logically. Be sure not to change the vocabulary word.*

1. Because she is <u>stout</u> of heart, she faces her future with great fear.

   _____

2. The film was 3 hours long with no <u>intermission</u>; we were grateful for the break.

   _____

3. He was cheerful as he recounted to us his many <u>woes</u> of the past year.

   _____

4. So many misfortunes in a single day caused her to <u>wail</u> with happiness.

   _____

B. DIRECTIONS: *On the line, write the letter of the choice that is the best synonym, or word with a similar meaning, for each numbered word.*

___ 1. wail
    A. strike
    B. publish
    C. grieve
    D. crawl

___ 2. woes
    A. signals
    B. factories
    C. songs
    D. sorrows

___ 3. intermission
    A. analysis
    B. break
    C. communication
    D. alliance

___ 4. stout
    A. plentiful
    B. sturdy
    C. weary
    D. energetic

Name _____ Date _____

Poetry by Alice Walker, Bashō, Chiyojo, Walt Whitman, William Shakespeare
Support for Writing to Compare

Use a chart like the one shown to make prewriting notes for an essay comparing the relationship between lyric form and meaning in two poems from the selections.

Title of Poem 1: _____ **Lyric Form:** _____ **Characteristics of Form:** _____ _____ _____ **Relationship of Poem's Form to Its Meaning:** _____ _____ _____ _____	
Title of Poem 2: _____ **Lyric Form:** _____ **Characteristics of Form:** _____ _____ _____ **Relationship of Poem's Form to Its Meaning:** _____ _____ _____ _____	

Gary L. Blackwood
Listening and Viewing

Segment 1: Meet Gary L. Blackwood
- What is *terra incognita,* and what does Gary L. Blackwood hope to accomplish by setting his stories there?
- What do you think you could learn by reading a story set in another place and time?

_____

_____

_____

_____

Segment 2: Drama
- What must Gary L. Blackwood do when transferring a story into a play?
- After listening to Gary L. Blackwood's reading of the book passage and a scene from the play, which do you prefer and why?

_____

_____

_____

_____

Segment 3: The Writing Process
- How do you think Gary L. Blackwood's acting experience has helped him as a playwright?
- How do you think this experience helps him write his sword fighting scenes?

_____

_____

_____

_____

Segment 4: The Rewards of Writing
- What messages does Gary L. Blackwood hope to convey through his writing?
- What message do you think it would be important to convey through your writing? Why?

_____

_____

_____

_____

Learning About Drama

A drama or play is a story written to be performed by actors. It features **characters** facing a **conflict,** or struggle, that propels the sequence of events called the **plot.** The conflict reaches a **climax,** the point of greatest tension, and then is resolved. The **dialogue,** or speeches of the characters, tells the story unlike fiction, in which the voice of a narrator tells the story.

The following chart shows some of the most important structural features and elements of drama.

Feature/Element	Function
acts and **scenes**	the basic units of drama
script	the play's text, containing dialogue and stage directions
stage directions	directions providing details about sets, lighting, sound effects, props, costumes, and acting
sets	constructions indicating where the drama takes place
props	movable objects that actors use onstage
theme	a drama's insight into life
dramatic effect	illusion of reality in a play's performance
dramatic speech	**monologue:** a long, uninterrupted speech delivered by a character to other characters who are on stage, but remain silent **soliloquy:** a speech in which a character alone on stage reveals private thoughts that the audience is allowed to overhear **aside:** a brief remark in which a character expresses private thoughts to the audience rather than to other characters

DIRECTIONS: *Circle the letter of the answer that best matches each numbered item.*

1. scenes
   A. directions to actors   B. props   C. subdivisions of acts
2. theme
   A. historical context   B. insight into life   C. dramatic speech
3. speech in which a character alone on stage reveals private thoughts and feelings
   A. dialogue   B. monologue   C. soliloquy
4. movable objects used on stage
   A. props   B. sets   C. asides
5. text of a play
   A. stage directions   B. dialogue   C. script
6. sequence of events in a drama
   A. climax   B. conflict   C. plot

Name _____ Date _____

from **The Shakespeare Stealer** by Gary L. Blackwood
Model Selection: Drama

In the script or text of a drama, playwrights combine **dialogue** with **stage directions** to tell the story, or plot, of the play. Stage directions are quickly recognizable because they are usually printed in italics and set off in brackets. When actors rehearse a play, they use the stage directions as a guide for delivering their lines, moving on stage, handling props, and using their posture and gestures to convey meaning.

DIRECTIONS: *Answer the following questions about* The Shakespeare Stealer *using the space provided.*

1. What specific information does the playwright provide in the stage directions at the beginning of Act I? Why would this information be helpful to the director and the actors?

   _____

   _____

   _____

   _____

2. Read the following excerpt from the play.

   WIDGE:

   Aye! It was a fortnight ago. 'A spotted me scribbling away, and afore I could make me escape, 'a collared me and snatched away me table-book!

   BRIGHT:

   Why did you not tell me this sooner?

   WIDGE:

   I was afeared. I kenned you'd be angry.

   What conflict between Widge and Bright does this passage reveal?

   _____

   _____

3. When Falconer enters in the first scene, what kind of mood or atmosphere do the stage directions suggest should be established on stage?

   _____

   _____

4. How does Blackwood use stage directions in the fight between Falconer and the thieves?

   _____

   _____

5. Toward the end of the excerpt, what plan is revealed in the dialogue between Simon Bass and Widge?

   _____

   _____

Name _____ Date _____

The Tragedy of Romeo and Juliet, *Act I,* by William Shakespeare
Literary Analysis: Dialogue and Stage Directions

Dialogue is conversation between or among characters. In prose, dialogue is usually set off with quotation marks. In drama, the dialogue generally follows the name of the speaker, as in this example:

> BENVOLIO. I aimed so near when I suppose you loved.
>
> ROMEO. A right good markman. And she's fair I love.

Dialogue reveals the personalities and relationships of the characters and advances the action of a play.

Stage directions are notes in the text of a play that describe how the work should be performed, or staged. These instructions are usually printed in italics and sometimes set in brackets or parentheses. They describe scenes, lighting, sound effects, and the appearance and physical actions of the characters, as in this example:

> *Scene iii.* FRIAR LAWRENCE's cell.
>
> [*Enter.* FRIAR LAWRENCE *alone, with a basket.*]

As you read, notice how the dialogue and stage directions work together to help you "see" and "hear" the play in your mind.

DIRECTIONS: *Read the following passages from Act I and then use the lines provided to answer the questions.*

> TYBALT. Patience perforce with willful choler meeting
> Makes my flesh tremble in their different greeting.
> I will withdraw; but this intrusion shall,
> Now seeming sweet, convert to bitt'rest gall. (Act I, Scene v, ll. 88–91)

1. In the context of the scene, what does Tybalt mean by "this intrusion"?

_____

2. What do the lines reveal about Tybalt's personality?

_____

_____

3. What do the lines foreshadow for the plot of the play?

_____

_____

_____

Name _____   Date _____

The Tragedy of Romeo and Juliet, *Act I,* by William Shakespeare
Reading: Use Text Aids to Summarize

Summarizing is briefly stating the main points in a piece of writing. Stopping periodically to summarize what you have read helps you to check your comprehension before you read further.

To be sure that you understand Shakespeare's language before you summarize long passages, **use text aids**—the numbered explanations that appear alongside the text.

- If you are confused by a passage, check to see if there is a footnote or side note and read the corresponding explanation.
- Reread the passage, using the information from the note to be sure you grasp the meaning of the passage.

DIRECTIONS: *Use the text aids to answer the following questions about what you read in Act I of the play.*

1. In your own words, summarize what is happening in Verona based on lines 1–4 of the Prologue.

   _____

   _____

   _____

2. In Scene i, as the two Montague Servingmen approach the two Capulet Servingmen, Sampson says, "Let us take the law of our sides; let them begin." What does he mean?

   _____

   _____

3. Later in Scene i, Benvolio and Montague talk about how unhappy Romeo has been. Then, they see Romeo. Benvolio tells Montague to leave so that he can talk to Romeo alone. Montague says, "I would thou wert so happy by thy stay / To hear true shrift." Put this wish into your own words.

   _____

   _____

4. In Scene iii, Juliet's mother tells her to "Read o'er the volume of young Paris's face." Refer to that passage (lines 81–92) and, with the help of text aids 9 and 10, restate the advice Lady Capulet gives to her daughter.

   _____

   _____

   _____

   _____

Name _____ Date _____

The Tragedy of Romeo and Juliet, *Act I,* by William Shakespeare
Vocabulary Builder

Word List

| pernicious | grievance | augmenting | transgression |

A. DIRECTIONS: *Match each word in Column A with the correct definition in Column B.*

Column A
___ 1. pernicious
___ 2. augmenting
___ 3. transgression
___ 4. grievance

Column B
A. wrongdoing
B. injustice
C. causing great injury
D. increasing

B. DIRECTIONS: *In each of the following items, think about the meaning of the italicized word and then answer the question.*

1. Would you be likely to praise an action that had *pernicious* consequences? Why or why not?
   _____

2. In your opinion, does a *transgression* typically deserve punishment? Explain.
   _____

3. Would a person expressing a *grievance* be likely to seem happy or sad? Explain.
   _____

4. If your employer announces that she is *augmenting* your salary, how would you feel?
   _____

C. DIRECTIONS: *On the line, write the letter of the choice that is the best synonym for each numbered word.*

___ 1. pernicious
   A. illicit
   B. immediate
   C. injurious
   D. indigenous

___ 2. transgression
   A. sin
   B. trophy
   C. effort
   D. reservation

___ 3. grievance
   A. lamentation
   B. testimony
   C. proclamation
   D. injustice

___ 4. augmenting
   A. gauging
   B. limiting
   C. increasing
   D. dividing

Name _____ Date _____

The Tragedy of Romeo and Juliet, *Act I*, by William Shakespeare
Support for Writing a Letter to an Advice Columnist

For your letter, use a chart such as the one shown to develop prewriting notes.

Who I Am (Romeo or Juliet): _____

Person Whom I Love: _____

Reasons Why I Think My Love Is Doomed:

1. _____
   _____

2. _____
   _____

3. _____
   _____

4. _____

Request for Advice: _____
_____

Response from Advice Columnist: _____
_____
_____
_____

Name _____ Date _____

The Tragedy of Romeo and Juliet, *Act II,* by William Shakespeare
Literary Analysis: Blank Verse

Blank verse is unrhymed poetry written in a meter called iambic pentameter. A line written in iambic pentameter includes five stressed syllables, each preceded by an unstressed syllable, as in the following example:

'Tis but thy name that is my enemy.

Thou art thyself though not a Montague.

Much of *The Tragedy of Romeo and Juliet* is written in blank verse. Shakespeare uses its formal meter to reinforce character rank. Important or aristocratic characters typically speak in blank verse. Minor or comic characters often do not speak in verse.

DIRECTIONS: *Mark the stressed and unstressed syllables in these lines from Act II, Scene v. Put a check mark next to the line that has one extra syllable and the line not written in iambic pentameter. The first line has been marked for you.*

JULIET. The clock struck nine when I did send the nurse,
In half an hour she promised to return.
Perchance she cannot meet him. That's not so.
O, she is lame! Love's heralds should be thoughts,
5 Which ten times faster glide than the sun's beams
Driving back shadows over low'ring hills.
Therefore do nimble-pinioned doves draw Love,
And therefore hath the wind-swift Cupid wings.
Now is the sun upon the highmost hill
10 Of this day's journey, and from nine to twelve
Is three long hours, yet she is not come.
Had she affections and warm youthful blood
She would be as swift in motion as a ball;
My words would bandy her to my sweet love,
15 And his to me.
But old folks, many feign as they were dead—
Unwieldy, slow, heavy and pale as lead.

Name _____ Date _____

The Tragedy of Romeo and Juliet, *Act II*, by William Shakespeare
Reading: Read in Sentences to Summarize

Summarizing is briefly stating the main points of a piece of writing. Stopping periodically to summarize what you have read helps you to check your comprehension before you read further.

Summarizing is especially useful when reading a play that has long passages of blank verse. When you encounter one of these passages, **read in sentences,** just as if you were reading a poem. Pause according to punctuation and not necessarily at the end of each line.

Once you have grasped the meanings of individual sentences in blank verse, you can more easily and more accurately summarize long passages.

DIRECTIONS: *Read the following passage and then answer the items on the lines provided.*

1 Two of the fairest stars in all the heaven,
2 Having some business, do entreat her eyes
3 To twinkle in their spheres till they return.
4 What if her eyes were there, they in her head?
5 The brightness of her cheek would shame those stars
6 As daylight doth a lamp; her eyes in heaven
7 Would through the airy region stream so bright
8 That birds would sing and think it were not night.

1. At the end of which line(s) should you make no pause at all?

   _____

2. At the end of which line(s) should you make a major pause?

   _____

3. At the end of which line(s) should you make a minor pause?

   _____

4. Write a brief summary of the main points in this passage.

   _____

   _____

   _____

   _____

   _____

The Tragedy of Romeo and Juliet, *Act II,* by William Shakespeare
Vocabulary Builder

Word List

procure	predominant	intercession
sallow	lamentable	unwieldly

A. DIRECTIONS: *Match each word in Column A with the correct definition in Column B.*

Column A

____ 1. sallow
____ 2. unwieldy
____ 3. procure
____ 4. intercession
____ 5. predominant
____ 6. lamentable

Column B

A. pleading on another's behalf
B. distressing
C. pale-yellowish
D. having great influence over others
E. clumsy
F. obtain

B. DIRECTIONS: *For each of the following items, think about the meaning of the italicized word and then answer the question.*

1. Would an *unwieldy* burden be easy or difficult to carry? Why?
   _____

2. If you received *lamentable* news, how would you feel?
   _____

3. Is *intercession* typically something you undertake on your own behalf or for the sake of someone else?
   _____

4. If a species of tree is *predominant* in your neighborhood, are there many or few of that species?
   _____

5. What might cause a person with a normally rosy complexion to suddenly look *sallow*?
   _____

6. If you need film for your camera, where might you try to *procure* it?
   _____

Name _____ Date _____

The Tragedy of Romeo and Juliet, *Act II,* by William Shakespeare
The Tragedy of Romeo and Juliet, *Act II,* by William Shakespeare
Support for Writing a Parody

For your parody, use a chart such as the one shown to develop prewriting notes.

Potentially Humorous Details: _____

_____

_____

_____

Main Focus for Parody: _____

_____

_____

Notes for Dialogue and Stage Directions: _____

_____

_____

_____

_____

_____

_____

_____

_____

_____

_____

_____

_____

_____

_____

Name _____ Date _____

The Tragedy of Romeo and Juliet, *Act III,* by William Shakespeare
Literary Analysis: Dramatic Speeches

Characters in plays often deliver these types of **dramatic speeches:**

- **Soliloquy:** a lengthy speech in which a character—usually alone on stage—expresses his or her true thoughts or feelings. Soliloquies are unheard by other characters.
- **Aside:** a brief remark by a character revealing his or her true thoughts or feelings, unheard by other characters.
- **Monologue:** a lengthy speech by one person. Unlike a soliloquy, a monologue is addressed to other characters.

Characters often add meaning to speeches by making **allusions**—references to well-known people, places, or events from mythology or literature. For example, in Act II, Mercutio insultingly calls Tybalt "Prince of Cats," alluding to a cat named Tybalt in French fables.

DIRECTIONS: *Answer the questions that follow about an aside, a soliloquy, a monologue, and an allusion.*

1. In Scene v, Juliet's mother refers to Romeo as a villain. In an aside, Juliet says, "Villain and he be many miles asunder." What is the effect of this aside? Why do you think Shakespeare wrote just the one remark as an aside?

   _____

   _____

2. In Scene v, Capulet delivers a monologue when he discovers that Juliet has rejected the match with Paris. Reread lines 177–197. What makes this speech a monologue?

   _____

   _____

3. Why is it important for Juliet and the others to hear Capulet's monologue?

   _____

   _____

4. At the close of Scene v, Juliet delivers a soliloquy. Reread lines 237–244. What makes these last eight lines a soliloquy?

   _____

   _____

5. Explain Juliet's allusion to Greek mythology in the opening lines of Scene ii.

   Gallop apace, you fiery-footed steeds,

   Toward Phoebus' lodging!

   _____

   _____

Name _____   Date _____

The Tragedy of Romeo and Juliet, *Act III,* by William Shakespeare
Reading: Use Paraphrases to Summarize

Summarizing is briefly stating the main points of a piece of writing. Before you summarize a long passage in a Shakespearean play, you should **paraphrase** it by restating the lines in your own words. For example, compare these two versions of a speech by Romeo:

Shakespeare's version: This gentleman, the prince's near ally, / My very friend, hath got his mortal hurt / In my behalf.

Paraphrase: My good friend, a close relative of the prince, has been fatally wounded in defending me.

Once you have paraphrased small portions of text, you can more easily and accurately summarize the entire passage.

DIRECTIONS: *Paraphrase the following passages from Act III. Remember that a paraphrase is a restatement in your own words for clarity. It is not a summary.*

1. **TYBALT.** Romeo, the love I bear thee can afford
   No better term than this: thou art a villain. (Scene i, ll. 56–57)

   _____

   _____

2. **PRINCE.** My blood for your rude brawls doth lie a-bleeding;
   But I'll amerce you with so strong a fine
   That you shall all repent the loss of mine. (Scene i, ll. 183–185)

   _____

   _____

   _____

3. **JULIET.** So tedious is this day
   As is the night before some festival
   To an impatient child that hath new robes
   And may not wear them. (Scene ii, ll. 28–31)

   _____

   _____

   _____

The Tragedy of Romeo and Juliet, *Act III,* by William Shakespeare
Vocabulary Builder

Word List

gallant	fray	martial
exile	eloquence	fickle

A. DIRECTIONS: *Match each word in Column A with the correct definition in Column B.*

Column A
___ 1. gallant
___ 2. exile
___ 3. martial
___ 4. fray
___ 5. eloquence
___ 6. fickle

Column B
A. noisy fight
B. changeable
C. graceful, persuasive speech
D. brave and noble
E. military
F. banish

B. DIRECTIONS: *For each of the following items, think about the meaning of the italicized word and then answer the question.*

1. Would you describe the people participating on both sides of a *fray* as hostile or friendly? Explain.

   _____

2. Can a romance in which one or both partners are *fickle* be described as stable and happy? Why or why not?

   _____

3. Would the sound of *martial* music evoke war or peace? Explain.

   _____

4. If you call someone *gallant,* is that a compliment or an insult? Explain.

   _____

5. What might be one of the main sorrows or complaints of a person who is *exiled*?

   _____

6. If a candidate delivers a speech with *eloquence,* is it likely to be persuasive? Why or why not?

   _____

Name _____ Date _____

Support for Writing an Editorial

For your editorial, use a chart such as the one shown to develop prewriting notes.

Notes on the Prince's Dialogue: _____

_____

_____

_____

My Opinion of the Prince's Sentencing of Romeo: _____

_____

_____

_____

Reasons to Support My Opinion: _____

_____

_____

_____

Details from Acts I–III to Include in Editorial:

1. _____

_____

_____

2. _____

_____

_____

3. _____

_____

_____

4. _____

_____

_____

212

The Tragedy of Romeo and Juliet, *Act III,* by William Shakespeare
Build Language Skills: Vocabulary

Word Roots: *labor*

The Latin word root -*labor*- means "work." Words that contain this word root have meanings related to work. For example, *elaborate* means "work out in great detail." You can help yourself remember the "detail" part of the definition by remembering that to add details (to elaborate) is more work than skipping the details.

A. DIRECTIONS: *Use a dictionary, if necessary, to look up the meanings of each of the following words or expressions containing the word root* labor. *Write one meaning for each item. Then, write a sentence using the word or expression in a context that makes its meaning clear.*

1. laboratory

   Meaning: _____

   Sentence: _____

2. Labor Day

   Meaning: _____

   Sentence: _____

3. labor union

   Meaning: _____

   Sentence: _____

4. labor camp

   Meaning: _____

   Sentence: _____

Academic Vocabulary Practice

B. DIRECTIONS: *Answer each question using the relevant vocabulary word.*

1. If you needed to *condense* a text, would you lengthen or shorten it?

   _____

2. If a detail is *relevant* to your main idea in an essay, should you include the detail or omit it?

   _____

3. If a persuasive argument you make in a speech evokes an *ambiguous* response in your audience, what conclusion can you draw about your listeners?

   _____

4. When you write a paragraph, what are ways to *elaborate* on the topic sentence?

   _____

5. Should the goal of a critical essay be to *illuminate* a literary work? Explain.

   _____

The Tragedy of Romeo and Juliet, *Act III,* by William Shakespeare
Build Language Skills: Grammar

Participles and Participle Phrases

A **participle** is a verb form that acts as an adjective.

There are two kinds of participles: present participles and past participles. **Present participles** end in *-ing.* The **past participles** of regular verbs end in *-ed.*

A **participial phase** is a group of words that functions as an adjective in a sentence and contains a participle.

Participle:	She glimpsed a *soaring* eagle. (modifies *eagle*)
Participial Phrase:	She glimpsed a bird *soaring high in the sky.* (modifies *bird*)

A. DIRECTIONS: *In the following sentences, identify each participle or participial phrase. Indicate the word each one modifies.*

1. Frightened by the prospect of a brawl, Benvolio urges Mercutio to go indoors.
   _____

2. Trying to protect Mercutio, Romeo actually causes Mercutio's death.
   _____

3. The feuding families are punished by the Prince.
   _____

4. Criticizing Juliet harshly, Capulet threatens to disown her.
   _____

5. Romeo, lamenting his fate, prepares to commit suicide.
   _____

B. Writing Application: *Write a brief paragraph about a trip or an excursion you have taken or would like to take. Use at least three participial phrases in your writing, and underline each participial phrase you use. Be careful to avoid misplaced modifiers.*

_____

_____

_____

_____

_____

_____

_____

_____

Unit 5 Resources: Drama

Name _____ Date _____

The Tragedy of Romeo and Juliet, *Act IV,* by William Shakespeare
Literary Analysis: Dramatic Irony

Dramatic irony is a contradiction between what a character thinks and says and what the audience or reader knows is true. For example, in Act III, Capulet plans Juliet's wedding to Paris. He does not know what you know: that Juliet is already married to Romeo. Dramatic irony involves the audience emotionally in the story.

Shakespeare knew his audience could become *too* involved in the intense emotion of *Romeo and Juliet.* Therefore, he made sure to include the following elements to lighten the play's mood:

- **Comic relief:** a technique used to interrupt a serious scene by introducing a humorous character or situation
- **Puns:** plays on words involving a word with multiple meanings or two words that sound alike but have different meanings. For example, the dying Mercutio makes a pun involving two meanings of the word *grave:* "Ask for me tomorrow, and you shall find me a grave man."

DIRECTIONS: *Use the lines provided to answer the following questions.*

1. Explain the dramatic irony in this passage from Scene i, when Friar Lawrence asks Paris to leave.

    FRIAR. My lord, we must entreat the time alone.
    PARIS. God shield I should disturb devotion!
       Juliet, on Thursday early will I rouse ye.

    _____

    _____

2. In Scene ii, Juliet tells her father she will go through with the wedding, and he begins to make preparations for the celebration. How do Capulet's words create dramatic irony?

    CAPULET. My heart is wondrous light,
       Since this same wayward girl is so reclaimed.

    _____

    _____

3. Juliet prepares for bed in Scene iii. Why is this exchange dramatically ironic?

    LADY CAPULET. What are you busy, ho? Need you my help?
    JULIET. No, madam, we have culled such necessaries
       As are behoveful for our state tomorrow. . . .
    LADY CAPULET. Good night.
       Get thee to bed, and rest: for thou hast need.

    _____

    _____

Name _____ Date _____

Reading: Break Down Long Sentences to Summarize

Summarizing is briefly stating the main points of a piece of writing. Stopping periodically to summarize what you have read helps you to check your comprehension before you read further.

Before you summarize a long passage of Shakespearean dialogue, you should **break down long sentences.**

- If a sentence contains multiple subjects or verbs, separate it into smaller sentences with one subject and one verb.
- If a sentence contains colons, semicolons, or dashes, treat those punctuation marks as periods in order to make smaller sentences.

DIRECTIONS: *Read the following passages. Practice breaking down the sentences by reading them in meaningful sections according to the punctuation. Rewrite the sentences in your own words, using smaller sentences.*

1. **PARIS.** Immoderately she weeps for Tybalt's death,
   And therefore have I little talked of love;
   For Venus smiles not in a house of tears. (Act IV, Scene i)

   _____

   _____

   _____

2. **JULIET.** 'Twixt my extremes and me this bloody knife
   Shall play the umpire, arbitrating that
   Which the commission of thy years and art
   Could to no issue of true honor bring. (Act IV, Scene i)

   _____

   _____

   _____

3. **FRIAR.** Hold, daughter. I do spy a kind of hope
   Which craves as desperate an execution
   As that is desperate which we would prevent.

   _____

   _____

   _____

The Tragedy of Romeo and Juliet, *Act IV,* by William Shakespeare
Vocabulary Builder

Word List

> pensive   enjoined   wayward
> dismal   loathsome

A. DIRECTIONS: *Match each word in Column A with the correct definition in Column B.*

Column A	Column B
___ 1. pensive	A. headstrong
___ 2. dismal	B. ordered
___ 3. loathsome	C. deeply thoughtful
___ 4. wayward	D. disgusting
___ 5. enjoined	E. causing gloom or misery

B. DIRECTIONS: *In each of the following items, think about the meaning of the italicized word and then answer the question.*

1. Would most of the people at a lively party be likely to be in a *pensive* mood? Why or why not?

   _____

2. If a good friend's behavior was *wayward*, would you be pleased or concerned? Explain.

   _____

3. "That place is *dismal*," he remarked. Would you want to go there? Why or why not?

   _____

4. If you were *enjoined* to do something, would the action be ordered or recommended?

   _____

5. If a swampland you were visiting had a *loathsome* smell, would you be tempted to return?

   _____

C. DIRECTIONS: *On the line, write the letter of the choice that is the best synonym for each numbered word.*

___ 1. dismal	___ 2. wayward
A. profound	A. eccentric
B. soothing	B. roomy
C. gloomy	C. itinerant
D. rarefied	D. headstrong

The Tragedy of Romeo and Juliet, *Act IV,* by William Shakespeare
Support for Writing an Abstract

For your abstract, or brief summary, use a chart such as the one shown to make notes.

Major Events in Acts I-IV: _____

_____

_____

_____

_____

Major Characters and Their Relationships: _____

_____

_____

_____

_____

Most Memorable Scene in Acts I-IV: _____

_____

_____

_____

_____

Overall Mood of the Play: _____

_____

_____

_____

Name _____ Date _____

The Tragedy of Romeo and Juliet, *Act V*, by William Shakespeare
Literary Analysis: Tragedy

A **tragedy** is a drama in which the central character, who is of noble stature, meets with disaster or great misfortune. The tragic hero's downfall is usually the result of one of the following:

- fate
- a serious character flaw
- some combination of both

Motive is an important element of a tragic hero's character. A character's motive is the reason behind an individual's thoughts or actions. In many of Shakespeare's tragedies, the hero's motives are basically good, but sometimes misguided. As a result, the hero suffers a tragic fate that may seem undeserved.

Although tragedies typically have unhappy endings, they can also be uplifting. They often show the greatness of which the human spirit is capable when faced with grave challenges.

DIRECTIONS: *Use the lines provided to answer the questions about tragedy and motive in* Romeo and Juliet.

1. In what ways does Romeo fit the characteristics of a tragic hero? How does he *not* fit these characteristics? In your answer, include a consideration of his tragic flaw.

   _____

   _____

   _____

   _____

   _____

2. The ancient Greek philosopher Aristotle, in his treatise on tragedy entitled *Poetics*, identified another element that is common to most tragedies: the hero's recognition of the whole tragic situation. This recognition always comes too late for the hero to avoid disaster or death. However, Shakespeare departs from Aristotle's idea about the hero's recognition. In *Romeo and Juliet,* it is not Romeo who experiences recognition, but other characters in the play. Who are these characters, and when does the recognition occur?

   _____

   _____

   _____

   _____

   _____

   _____

Name _____   Date _____

The Tragedy of Romeo and Juliet, *Act V*, by William Shakespeare
Reading: Identify Causes and Effects to Summarize

Summarizing is briefly stating the main points of a piece of writing. In summarizing the action in a tragedy, it is useful to first **identify causes and effects.**

- A *cause* is an event, an action, or a feeling that produces a result.
- An *effect* is the result produced by the cause.

Tragedies often involve a chain of cause and effects that advances the plot and leads to the final tragic outcome. Understanding how one event leads to another will help you to summarize complicated plots like the one in *Romeo and Juliet*.

DIRECTIONS: As you read Act V, fill in the boxes in this chain-of-events graphic organizer. The first event of each scene is filled in for you. Note that Scene iii has two chains of events. When your chain-of-events graphic is complete, notice how the events in one scene have produced events in later scenes.

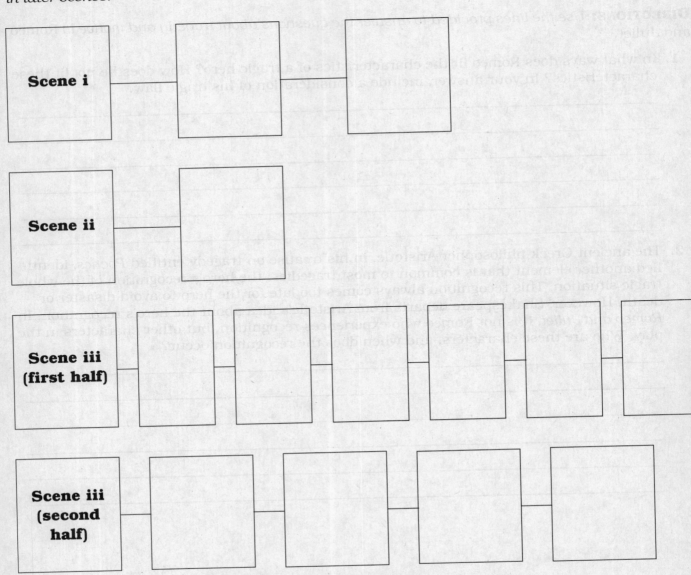

The Tragedy of Romeo and Juliet, *Act V,* by William Shakespeare
Vocabulary Builder

Word List

| remnants ambiguities penury |
| haughty scourge |

A. DIRECTIONS: *Match each word in Column A with the correct definition in Column B.*

Column A

___ 1. remnants
___ 2. haughty
___ 3. penury
___ 4. ambiguities
___ 5. scourge

Column B

A. unclear statements
B. instrument for inflicting punishment
C. remainders
D. arrogant
E. extreme poverty

B. DIRECTIONS: *In each of the following items, think about the meaning of the italicized word and then answer the question.*

1. Would someone living in *penury* be likely to purchase an expensive new home? Why or why not?

_____

2. If a statement contains *ambiguities*, can you be sure of its meaning? Explain.

_____

3. Would the sight of a *scourge* inspire happiness or fear?

_____

4. If an area is pounded by the *remnants* of a hurricane, does it experience winds in advance of the storm or after the storm?

_____

5. Would you praise or criticize someone for *haughty* behavior? Explain.

_____

C. DIRECTIONS: *On the line, write the letter of the choice that is the best synonym for each numbered word.*

___ 1. haughty
A. mighty
B. respectful
C. arrogant
D. morose

___ 2. scourge
A. whip
B. insult
C. outbreak
D. cleanser

Name _____ Date _____

The Tragedy of Romeo and Juliet, *Act V,* by William Shakespeare
Support for Writing a Persuasive Letter

For your persuasive letter, use a chart such as the one shown to develop prewriting notes.

Announcement of Marriage Ceremony: _____

_____

Opinion Statement (Aim of Letter): _____

_____

Persuasive Appeals

1. Factual evidence: _____

_____

_____

_____

_____

2. Emotional Appeals: _____

_____

_____

_____

_____

The Tragedy of Romeo and Juliet, *Act V,* by William Shakespeare
Build Language Skills: Vocabulary

The Latin Root *-lum-*

The root *-lum-* means "light." Words that contain the word root *-lum-* have meanings related to light. For example, *illuminate* means, literally, "brings light to." It is often used in the figurative sense: When a fact or idea is brought to light, it is *illuminated,* or clarified.

A. DIRECTIONS: *Look up the meanings of the following words. Write one meaning for each word. Then, write a sentence using the word in a context that makes its meaning clear.*

1. luminous

   Meaning: _____

   Sentence: _____

2. luminary

   Meaning: _____

   Sentence: _____

3. luminaria

   Meaning: _____

   Sentence: _____

4. illumination

   Meaning: _____

   Sentence: _____

Academic Vocabulary Practice

B. DIRECTIONS: *Follow the instructions to write sentences containing the academic vocabulary words.*

1. Use *condense* in a sentence about writing a summary of a short story.

   _____

2. Use *relevant* in a sentence about a research report.

   _____

3. Use *ambiguous* in a sentence about a newspaper headline.

   _____

4. Use *elaborate* in a sentence about a persuasive speech.

   _____

5. Use *illuminate* in a sentence about the hero of a detective story.

   _____

The Tragedy of Romeo and Juliet, *Act V,* by William Shakespeare
Build Language Skills: Grammar

Gerund and Gerund Phrase

A **gerund** is a form of a verb that acts as a noun. It can function as a subject, an object, a predicate noun, or the object of a preposition. A **gerund phrase** is a gerund and its modifiers that acts as a noun.

Look at the following examples:

Gerund:	*Singing* was a delight. (subject)
Gerund Phrase:	*Singing with the community chorus* was a way to make new friends. (subject)
	We always took pleasure in *attending the rehearsals on Friday nights.* (object of preposition)

A. DIRECTIONS: *In the following sentences, identify each gerund or gerund phrase, and identify its function.*

1. Rehearsing weekly was a necessity.

   _____

2. Selecting that song was my idea.

   _____

3. Our audience remained loyal, but it showed no signs of expanding.

   _____

4. For weeks, we worked toward the goal of presenting a special Thanksgiving concert.

   _____

5. Maria practices playing the piano for several hours each day.

   _____

B. Writing Application: *Write a brief paragraph describing one of your favorite films or television shows. Use at least three gerund phrases in your writing, and underline each gerund phrase you use.*

_____

_____

_____

_____

_____

_____

_____

_____

"Pyramus and Thisbe" by Ovid
Scenes from dramatic works by William Shakespeare
Literary Analysis: Archetypal Theme—Ill-fated Love

An **archetype** is a plot, a character, an image, or a setting that appears in literature from around the world and throughout history. Archetypes represent truths about life and are said to mirror the working of the human mind. Common archetypes include the following:

- *Characters:* the hero; the outcast
- *Plot types:* the quest, or search; the task
- *Symbol:* water as a symbol for life; fire as a symbol of power

A **theme** is the central idea, message, or insight of a literary work. **Archetypal themes** are those that develop or explore foundational, archetypal ideas. One example of an archetypal theme is ill-fated love, which appears in folklore, mythology, and literature from all over the world.

Works of literature may differ in their presentations of the same archetypal theme for a variety of reasons, including the following:

- the values of the author and the audience at the time the literary work was written
- the author's purpose for writing the literary work
- the culture and language of the author, including any literary styles and expectations

DIRECTIONS: *Write your answers to the following questions on the lines provided.*

1. In what sense are all three of these works stories of ill-fated love: *Romeo and Juliet*, "Pyramus and Thisbe," and the tale of Titania and Bottom's love in *A Midsummer Night's Dream*?

   _____

   _____

   _____

2. Why do you think Shakespeare added Romeo and Juliet's marriage to his story?

   _____

   _____

   _____

3. What message about love does Titania's love for Bottom suggest?

   _____

   _____

   _____

4. Which version of the archetypal theme of ill-fated love do you think best reflects the nature of love? Explain.

   _____

   _____

   _____

   _____

"**Pyramus and Thisbe**" by Ovid
Scenes from dramatic works by William Shakespeare
Vocabulary Builder

Word List

| lament | inevitable | enamored | enthralled |

A. DIRECTIONS: *Revise each sentence so that the underlined vocabulary word is used logically. Be sure not to change the vocabulary word.*

1. We heard the mourners' <u>lament</u> and saw them smiling.

   _____

2. Since the defeat of our team in the big game was <u>inevitable</u>, we planned a victory celebration.

   _____

3. Mr. Schuyler nodded his agreement and said he was not <u>enamored</u> of our plan.

   _____

4. We sat <u>enthralled</u> as the lecturer droned on, endlessly repeating himself.

   _____

B. DIRECTIONS: *On the line, write the letter of the choice that is the best antonym, or opposite, for each word.*

___ 1. inevitable
   A. available
   B. presentable
   C. avoidable
   D. grotesque

___ 2. enamored
   A. charmed
   B. gratified
   C. assumed
   D. disgusted

___ 3. enthralled
   A. bored
   B. attracted
   C. captured
   D. amused

___ 4. lament
   A. predict
   B. celebrate
   C. protest
   D. despise

"Pyramus and Thisbe" by Ovid
Scenes from dramatic works by William Shakespeare
Support for Writing to Compare

Use a chart like the one shown to make prewriting notes for an essay comparing and contrasting Shakespeare's treatment of the characters and events from "Pyramus and Thisbe" in *Romeo and Juliet* and in *A Midsummer Night's Dream*.

	Romeo and Juliet	*A Midsummer Night's Dream*
How Characters Affect Archetypal Theme		
How Settings Affect Archetypal Theme		
How Shakespeare Wanted Audience to Feel About Ill-fated Love		

Possible Reasons for Exploring the Same Story in a Tragedy and in a Comedy:

_____

_____

_____

_____

Name _____ Date _____

"The Inspector-General" by Anton Chekhov
Literary Analysis: Comedy

Comedy is a form of drama that ends happily, and aims primarily to amuse. The humor in comic plays may arise from one or more of the following elements: funny names, witty dialogue, and comic situations, such as deception by a character, misunderstandings, or mistaken identities.

The humor of comic situations often relies on **dramatic irony,** which is a contradiction between what a character thinks and says and what the audience knows is true. In comedies, the audience often knows the truth about a situation while the characters remain unaware. As a result, the characters' statements and behavior may seem funny to the audience.

DIRECTIONS: *Read each passage. Then, briefly explain why it is humorous or comic.*

1. **STORYTELLER.** And when he'd thought to himself for long enough, he fell into conversation with the driver of the cart. What did he talk about? About himself, of course. [*Exit the* STORYTELLER.]
   TRAVELER. I gather you've got a new Inspector-General in these parts.

   _____

   _____

   _____

2. **DRIVER.** Oh, no, the new one goes everywhere on the quiet, like. Creeps around like a cat. Don't want no one to see him, don't want no one to know who he is.

   _____

   _____

   _____

3. **DRIVER.** He hops on a train just like anyone else, just like you or me. Then when he gets off, he don't go jumping into a cab or nothing fancy. Oh, no. He wraps himself up from head to toe so you can't see his face, and he wheezes away like an old dog so no one can recognize his voice.
   TRAVELER. Wheezes? That's not wheezing! That's the way he talks! So I gather.

   _____

   _____

   _____

4. **DRIVER.** Fixed himself up a tube behind his desk, he has. Leans down, takes a pull on it, no one the wiser.
   TRAVELER [*offended*]. How do you know all this, may I ask?

   _____

   _____

   _____

Name _____ Date _____

"The Inspector-General" by Anton Chekhov
Reading: Draw Conclusions

A **conclusion** is a decision or an opinion that you reach based on details in a text. In drawing conclusions, you consider both stated and implied information. To draw conclusions about characters in a play, **use both dialogue and stage directions** to find meaningful information.

- Consider what characters' words suggest about their personalities and circumstances.
- Read stage directions closely for details about the scene, characters' appearances, and characters' behavior. Take note of other information that could prove essential to the plot or ideas expressed in the play.

DIRECTIONS: As you read The Inspector-General, use the following chart to gather information and draw conclusions about the traveler's identity. Then, use the evidence you have gathered to answer the questions that follow the chart.

Evidence of the Traveler's Appearance and of What He Says and Does:	Conclusions From the Evidence:
Example: The Traveler wears dark glasses and a long overcoat with its collar turned up.	He is traveling incognito and does not want his identity to be known.
1. _____	1. _____
2. _____	2. _____
3. _____	3. _____
4. _____	4. _____

5. Who is the traveler?

6. What is his reason for traveling incognito?

_____

7. What conclusion can you draw about the traveler's attitude toward his work?

_____

8. What does the evidence suggest about the traveler's expectations?

_____

_____

9. What conclusions can you draw about the traveler's character?

_____

_____

Unit 5 Resources: Drama

Name _____ Date _____

"The Inspector-General" by Anton Chekhov
Vocabulary Builder

Word List

anonymous	trundle
discreetly	cunning

A. DIRECTIONS: *Answer each of the following questions.*

1. Which of the following most nearly means the opposite of *discreetly*?
   A. conspicuously   B. pompously   C. tactfully   D. quietly

2. Which of the following most nearly means the opposite of *cunning*?
   A. sly   B. naive   C. agile   D. smart

3. Which of the following is the best synonym for *anonymous*?
   A. persuasive   B. temporary   C. nameless   D. shy

4. If a cart begins to *trundle*, what does it do?
   A. stops short   C. rolls along
   B. jerks and jounces   D. falls over

B. DIRECTIONS: *In each of the following items, think about the meaning of the italicized word and then answer the question.*

1. Which would be more likely to *trundle*, a cart or a horse? Why?

   _____

2. Is it easy or difficult to reply directly to the writer of an *anonymous* letter? Why?

   _____

3. If you perform a task *discreetly*, do you usually attract the notice of other people? Why or why not?

   _____

4. Is a *cunning* person likely to be candid or deceptive?

   _____

Name _____ Date _____

"The Inspector-General" by Anton Chekhov
Support for Writing a Play

As you prepare to write a **play** about students outwitting a bully, think about how you can make the school setting seem real. Make sure that the dialogue sounds like words and phrases that could be used by actual students.

In your play, use *dramatic irony*—that is, include information that is clear to the audience but not known by the character of the bully. Make your play entertaining and educational. Teach the lesson that it is always important to be kind, even to a bully. Use the chart below to help you organize your ideas.

Setting of the play: _____
Major characters (describe the main traits of each): _____   _____   _____   _____   _____
Basic plot of the play: How the bully behaves toward others: _____   _____   _____   _____
How other students plan to outwit the bully: _____   _____   _____
Dramatic irony (what the audience knows that is not known to the bully): _____   _____
How the problem is resolved: _____
What you want the audience to learn from your play: _____   _____

Use additional sheets of paper to write the first scene of your play. Remember that you should include exciting action and dialogue that could be performed on stage.

Name _____ Date _____

"The Inspector-General" by Anton Chekhov
Build Language Skills: Vocabulary

The Latin Roots -vis- and -vinc-

The Latin roots -vis- and its variant -vid- mean "see." Words that contain these roots, such as *visible* and *video*, have meanings related to seeing. The root -vinc-, along with its variant -vict-, means "conquer." For example, to *convince* someone, your argument should be stronger.

A. DIRECTIONS: *Use a dictionary, if necessary, to look up the meanings of each of the following words containing the word roots -vis-, -vid-, -vince-, and -vict-. Write one meaning for each word. Then, write a sentence using the word in a context that makes its meaning clear.*

1. vista

 Meaning: _____

 Sentence: _____

2. video

 Meaning: _____

 Sentence: _____

3. invincible

 Meaning: _____

 Sentence: _____

4. evince

 Meaning: _____

 Sentence: _____

Academic Vocabulary Practice

B. DIRECTIONS: *Answer each question using the relevant vocabulary word.*

1. If you *revise* a story, do you usually make changes in it?

 _____

2. If an editorial *convinces* you, do you find the writer's arguments persuasive?

 _____

3. When you *implement* a plan, do you put it into effect or do you send it back to the planners for further research?

 _____

4. Would you be likely to solve a problem if you had a practical *strategy* in mind?

 _____

5. What do you do when you *compile* research sources for a bibliography or works-cited list?

 _____

Name _____ Date _____

Build Language Skills: Grammar

Main and Subordinate Clauses

A **clause** is a group of words with a subject and a verb. A **main,** or **independent, clause** is a complete sentence. A **subordinate clause** has a subject and a verb but is not a complete thought.

A clause, a group of words that contains a subject and a verb, can be a main (independent) clause or a subordinate (dependent) clause. If the group of words needs additional information to make sense, it is a subordinate clause. Subordinate clauses can function as noun, adjective, or adverbial clauses. In the following examples, the main clause is underlined and the subordinate clause is italicized.

Main Clause:	The Internet is expanding.
Main Clause, Subordinate Clause:	It offers more and more *as time passes.*
Subordinate Clause, Main Clause:	*If we let it,* the Internet can change our lives.

A. DIRECTIONS: *Identify the subordinate clause in each sentence. Then, tell whether the subordinate clause functions as an adjective clause, an adverb clause, or a noun clause.*

1. Anton Chekhov began to write humorous sketches and short stories while he was studying medicine in Moscow.

_____

2. His best-known plays, which include *The Seagull* and *The Cherry Orchard,* are notable for their wistful, bittersweet irony.

_____

3. That Chekhov regarded others with tenderness and compassion is clearly evident in his stories and plays.

_____

4. In *The Inspector-General,* much of the humor springs from the traveler's ignorance that he has already been recognized.

_____

B. Writing Application: *Write a paragraph describing why you might like to undertake a journey incognito. Use at least three subordinate clauses in your writing, and underline each subordinate clause you use. Be prepared to tell whether each clause functions as an adjective, as an adverb, or as a noun.*

_____

_____

_____

_____

_____

from **The Importance of Being Earnest** by Oscar Wilde

from **Big Kiss** by Henry Alford

Literary Analysis: Satire

Satire is writing that exposes and makes fun of the foolishness and faults of an individual, an institution, a society, or a situation. Although a satire often makes readers laugh, it may also aim to correct the flaws that it criticizes. Some satires address serious social problems, while others address less important issues. Satirical writings vary in style and tone.

- A satire may be gentle and sympathetic or angry and bitter in tone. The tone will reflect the writer's attitude toward the subject.
- A satire may use **sarcasm** or **irony**—language that is "tongue-in-cheek" and means the opposite of what it says on the surface.
- A satire may **exaggerate** faults in order to make them both funny and obvious.

In addition, some satirists write as outside onlookers, while others include themselves as targets of the satire.

DIRECTIONS: *The following passages are from* The Importance of Being Earnest *and* Big Kiss. *Read each passage and think about it in the context of the selection as a whole. Then, write a brief phrase or statement that explains what the target of satire is in the passage. Add a comment on the satire's tone, and indicate whether the author includes himself as an object of satire.*

1. **GWENDOLEN.** We live, as I hope you know, Mr. Worthing, in an age of ideals. The fact is constantly mentioned in the more expensive monthly magazines, and has reached the provincial pulpits, I am told; and my ideal has always been to love someone of the name of Ernest. There is something in that name that inspires absolute confidence. The moment Algernon first mentioned to me that he had a friend called Ernest, I knew I was destined to love you. (*The Importance of Being Earnest*)

_____

_____

_____

_____

2. But five minutes later an assistant director who had assembled about a hundred of us in front of Federal Hall took away my camera.

"I based my character interpretation on that!" I exclaimed, hoping that this would translate to him as "Serious actor. Could handle a line of dialogue."

"I need it for up front," he reported tersely, then walked to the front of the crowd.

One of my fellow colleagues . . . witnessed my loss of camera and counseled, "You were probably overpropped anyway."

"Yes," I responded. "My work was getting proppy." (*Big Kiss*)

_____

_____

_____

_____

from **The Importance of Being Earnest** by Oscar Wilde
from **Big Kiss** by Henry Alford
Vocabulary Builder

Word List

| demonstrative | ignorance | allotment | assiduous |

A. DIRECTIONS: *Revise each sentence so that the underlined vocabulary word is used logically. Be sure not to change the vocabulary word.*

1. She is not especially <u>demonstrative</u>, so it is easy to know what she is feeling.

   _____

2. <u>Ignorance</u> of addition is a requirement for taking algebra.

   _____

3. The huge <u>allotment</u> of books from a generous donor required the library to reduce the number of shelves.

   _____

4. Teresa was so <u>assiduous</u> that she studied for about two minutes for the final exam.

   _____

B. DIRECTIONS: *On the line, write the letter of the choice that is the best definition for each word.*

___ 1. assiduous
    A. transient
    B. glossy
    C. diligent
    D. slapdash

___ 2. demonstrative
    A. childishly demanding
    B. naively taking risks
    C. showing feelings openly
    D. acting playfully

___ 3. allotment
    A. chance
    B. share
    C. majority
    D. minority

___ 4. ignorance
    A. lack of time
    B. lack of knowledge
    C. bad luck
    D. hunger

Name _____   Date _____

from The Importance of Being Earnest by Oscar Wilde
from Big Kiss by Henry Alford
Support for Writing to Compare

Use a chart like the one shown to make prewriting notes for an essay discussing the effect of point of view in each of the satires.

Writer's Purpose and Perspective

	Wilde, *The Importance of Being Earnest*	Alford, *Big Kiss*
Target of Satire		
Purpose of Satire		
Writer: Participant/ Nonparticipant		
Attitude Towards Characters		

Ways in Which Writer's Perspective Shapes the Satire

How does each writer create humor and present insights? _____

_____

_____

How does the writer's participation or lack of participation in the action affect the audience's sympathy for characters? _____

_____

_____

My Evaluation of the Satires _____

_____

_____

_____

Dean Smith
Listening and Viewing

Segment 1: Meet Dean Smith
- What is the meaning of "the Carolina way"?
- How do you think Dean Smith's philosophy of "play hard, play smart, play together" also applies to life off of the basketball court?

_____

_____

_____

Segment 2: Themes in Literature
- Why do you think sports writing is an important form of literature?
- What can Dean Smith and John Kilgo's book *The Carolina Way* teach its readers?

_____

_____

_____

Segment 3: The Writing Process
- How did Dean Smith and John Kilgo work together to write books?
- What benefits and challenges exist when writing a book with a coauthor?

_____

_____

_____

Segment 4: The Rewards of Writing
- How has writing been personally rewarding for both Dean Smith and John Kilgo?
- Have you ever read a piece of sports literature that has had a memorable impact on you as a reader? Explain.

_____

_____

_____

Learning About Themes in Literature

Before there was written literature, stories and poems were passed down by **oral** tradition—from generation to generation by word of mouth. Many tales expressed basic human emotions and explored **universal themes,** or insights into life that are true for many different times and cultures. Among such themes are the importance of heroism, the power of love, the strength of loyalty, and the dangers of greed.

Storytellers explored such themes by means of **archetypes.** An archetype is a situation, a character, an image, or a symbol that appears in the tales of various cultures. For example, the hero's quest, the struggle between good and evil, and tricksters appear in the stories of many different cultures and times. The circle is another archetype, a symbol of loyalty, protection, and completion, as in Odysseus' return to his homeland, Ithaca. The **historical context** (the social and cultural background of a particular tale) influences the presentation of archetypes.

The following are important narrative forms that express universal themes. A **myth** is a tale explaining the actions of gods and the humans who interact with them. Myths explain the causes of a natural phenomenon. **Folk tales** are brief stories focusing on human or animal heroes and are not primarily concerned with gods or the creation of the world. A **legend** recounts the adventures of a human hero and may be based on historical fact. **Tall tales** are legends told in an exaggerated way, intended for entertainment. An **epic** is a long narrative poem about a larger-than-life hero who goes on a dangerous journey or quest that is important to the history of a group or culture.

DIRECTIONS: *Circle the letter of the answer that best matches each numbered item.*

1. historical context
   A. author's biography
   B. story's cultural background
   C. story's theme

2. archetype
   A. story element in many cultures
   B. universal theme
   C. hero

3. tall tale
   A. epic   B. exaggerated folk tale   C. story featuring monsters

4. epic
   A. factual narrative   B. legend   C. long narrative poem

5. the power of love
   A. universal theme   B. oral tradition   C. historical context

6. quest
   A. hero's journey   B. story that explains   C. opposing person or force

7. main character in a folk tale
   A. historical figure   B. human or animal hero   C. god or goddess

"Play Hard; Play Together; Play Smart" *from* **The Carolina Way**
by Dean Smith with John Kilgo

Model Selection: Themes in Literature

Stories, poems, and essays often offer **themes,** or central insights into human life or behavior. The theme of a work may be directly stated by the author. More often, however, it is implied or suggested indirectly. The reader must use clues from the writer's choice of details, as well as from the style and tone of the work, to infer the theme.

Narratives, poems, and essays usually express the **values,** ideals, and behaviors cherished by the society in which they are produced. **Shared values** are held in common by people across cultures, and literary works give voice to them by exploring **universal themes**. In contrast, **culturally distinct values** are specific to a group. In a literary work, **cultural details** are the beliefs, traditions, and customs that reflect a particular society. Modern fiction and nonfiction, though written by individuals rather than fashioned by a group, can also express universal themes.

DIRECTIONS: *Use the space provided to answer the following questions about "Play Hard; Play Together; Play Smart."*

1. What are three cultural values stressed by Dean Smith in the essay?

   _____

   _____

   _____

   _____

2. Dean Smith coached American college basketball in the second half of the twentieth century. Do you think the values he emphasizes in his essay are culturally distinct, or are they shared values found in cultures around the world, in the past and present? Explain your answer in a few sentences.

   _____

   _____

   _____

   _____

   _____

   _____

3. Do Smith's main ideas in the essay suggest one or more universal themes? Write a paragraph in which you give your opinion about whether or not his essay contains universal themes. Use reasons and examples to support your position.

   _____

   _____

   _____

   _____

   _____

   _____

Name _____   Date _____

from **the Odyssey,** *Part 1* **by Homer**
Literary Analysis: Epic Hero

An **epic hero** is the larger-than-life central character in an epic—a long narrative poem about important events in the history or folklore of a nation or culture. Through adventurous deeds, the epic hero demonstrates traits—such as loyalty, honor, and resourcefulness—that are valued by the society in which the epic originates.

Many epics begin *in medias res* ("in the middle of things"), meaning that much of the important action in the story occurred before the point at which the poem begins. Therefore, an epic hero's adventures are often recounted in a **flashback,** a scene that interrupts the sequence of events in a narrative to relate earlier events. Flashbacks also allow the poet to provide a more complete portrait of the epic hero's character.

DIRECTIONS: *Consider the adventures shown in the left column of the following chart. Then, determine what evidence is contained in each adventure to support the position that Odysseus has the superior physical and mental prowess to be an epic hero. Write your answers in the chart.*

Adventure	Evidence of Mental Prowess	Evidence of Physical Prowess
1. The Lotus-Eaters		
2. The Cyclops		
3. The Sirens		
4. Scylla and Charybdis		

from **the Odyssey,** *Part 1* by Homer
Reading: Analyze the Influence of Historical and Cultural Context

The **historical and cultural context** of a work is the backdrop of details of the time and place in which the work is set or in which it was written. These details include the events, beliefs, and customs of a specific culture and time. When you read a work from another time and culture, **use background and prior knowledge** to analyze the influence of the historical and cultural context.

- Read the author biography, footnotes, and other textual aids to understand the work's historical and cultural context.
- Note how characters' behavior and attitudes reflect that context.

DIRECTIONS: *Answer the following questions on the lines provided.*

1. What does the common noun *odyssey* mean? Use a dictionary, if necessary, to look up this word and identify its meaning. How does this word relate to Homer's epic and the hero Odysseus?

   _____

   _____

   _____

2. What does the word *Homeric* mean? How does this word relate to the ancient Greek epics the *Iliad* and the *Odyssey*?

   _____

   _____

   _____

3. About when were the Homeric epics composed, or when did they assume their final form after centuries of development in the oral tradition?

   _____

   _____

4. Reread Odysseus' description of the Cyclops in Part 1, lines 109–120. What does this passage imply about ancient Greek values and beliefs? Explain your answer in a brief paragraph.

   _____

   _____

   _____

   _____

   _____

   _____

   _____

from the Odyssey, *Part 1* by Homer
Vocabulary Builder

Word List

plundered	dispatched	assuage	bereft
ardor	mammoth	insidious	

A. DIRECTIONS: *In each of the following items, think about the meaning of the italicized word and then answer the question.*

1. If you regard someone as *insidious*, do you like or dislike that person? Why?

   _____

2. Historically, when do people tend to *plunder*—during wartime or peacetime?

   _____

3. If Maria *dispatched* her assignment, did it take her a long time or a short time to finish?

   _____

4. Would you use gentle words or provocative words to *assuage* someone's anger or demands? Explain.

   _____

5. If you were *bereft* of sleep, would you feel fatigued or well-rested?

   _____

B. DIRECTIONS: *On the line, write the letter of the choice that is the best synonym for each numbered word.*

___ 1. bereft
   A. desperate
   B. delegated
   C. deprived
   D. determined

___ 2. mammoth
   A. illusory
   B. huge
   C. ridiculous
   D. cuddly

___ 3. insidious
   A. treacherous
   B. ominous
   C. unattractive
   D. enormous

___ 4. plundered
   A. attacked
   B. provoked
   C. robbed
   D. designed

___ 5. dispatched
   A. did habitually
   B. embarked on
   C. experimented with
   D. finished quickly

___ 6. ardor
   A. passionate enthusiasm
   B. bitter antagonism
   C. stubborn opposition
   D. astonished disbelief

Name _____ Date _____

from **the Odyssey,** *Part 1* by Homer
Support for Writing an Everyday Epic

Use a chart like the one below to jot down notes for your everyday epic.

Everyday Event:
_____

Epic Dimensions (adventure, bravery, life-and-death challenges): _____
_____
_____
_____
_____

Multiple Points of View: _____
_____
_____

Supernatural/Fantastic Elements: _____
_____
_____
_____
_____

Ideas for Performance/Recitation: _____
_____
_____
_____
_____
_____

from **the *Odyssey, Part 1*** by Homer
Build Language Skills: Vocabulary

Context Clues

Knowing that the prefix *contra-* means "against" provides a clue to the meaning of the word *controversy*, which means "parties having opinions against each other."

Example: There is a *controversy* over who actually wrote the Shakespearean plays.

A. DIRECTIONS: *Use a dictionary, if necessary, to look up the meanings of each of the following words containing the prefix* contra-. *Write one meaning for each word. Then, write a sentence using the word in a context that makes its meaning clear.*

1. contraband

   Meaning: _____

   Sentence: _____

2. contradistinction

   Meaning: _____

   Sentence: _____

3. contrariwise

   Meaning: _____

   Sentence: _____

4. contraindicate

   Meaning: _____

   Sentence: _____

Academic Vocabulary Practice

B. DIRECTIONS: *Answer each question using the relevant Academic Vocabulary word.*

1. If you are involved in a *controversy*, what can you expect?

   _____

2. Does a *technique* typically involve both a method and a skill?

   _____

3. When you *appraise* a literary work, do you analyze it or do you evaluate it?

   _____

4. If evidence *confirms* a theory, would you be inclined to accept or reject the theory?

   _____

5. Does a *complex* character in a literary work possess many conflicting personality traits or a single trait?

   _____

Name _____ Date _____

from the Odyssey, *Part 1* by Homer
Build Language Skills: Grammar

Simple and Compound Sentences

A **simple sentence** consists of a single independent clause. Although a simple sentence is just one independent clause with one subject and verb, the subject, verb, or both may be compound. A simple sentence may have modifying phrases and complements. However, it cannot have a subordinate clause.

> **Example:** Odysseus returned to Ithaca and took his revenge on the suitors. (simple sentence with compound verb)

A **compound sentence** consists of two or more independent clauses. The clauses can be joined by a comma and a coordinating conjunction or by a semicolon. Like a simple sentence, a compound sentence contains no subordinate clauses.

> **Example:** The suitors reveled in the hall; in the meantime, Penelope questioned the disguised Odysseus.

A. DIRECTIONS: *Identify each sentence as simple or compound.*

1. In his monumental epic, the *Odyssey,* Homer recounts the wanderings of Odysseus on his journey home to Ithaca after the Trojan War. _____

2. Odysseus enjoys the favor of the goddess Athena, but his safe return is jeopardized by the hostility of Poseidon, the sea god. _____

3. Odysseus foolishly leads his men into the cave of the Cyclops; there, several of them meet a ghastly fate. _____

4. Odysseus tricks the Cyclops by telling him a false name: "Nohbdy." _____

5. At the end of this adventure, however, Odysseus boastfully reveals his true name, thereby making himself vulnerable to the Cyclops' curse. _____

B. Writing Application: *On the following lines, write a paragraph in which you describe what you would wish for if you had three wishes. In your writing, use both simple and compound sentences. Be prepared to identify each type of sentence.*

_____

_____

_____

_____

_____

_____

_____

_____

_____

from the Odyssey, *Part 2* by Homer
Literary Analysis: Epic Simile

An **epic simile** is an elaborate comparison that may extend for several lines. Epic similes may use the words *like, as, just as,* or *so* to make the comparison. Unlike a normal simile, which draws a comparison to a single, distinct image, an epic simile is longer and more involved. It might recall an entire place or story. Epic similes are sometimes called Homeric similes.

DIRECTIONS: *Read the epic similes that follow. Then, circle the letter of the answer that best completes each sentence.*

A. But the man skilled in all ways of contending,
satisfied by the great bow's look and heft,
like a musician, like a harper, when
with quiet hand upon his instrument
he draws between his thumb and forefinger
a sweet new string upon a peg: so effortlessly
Odysseus in one motion strung the bow.

1. In the passage, what extended comparison does Homer use to complete this analogy:
   archer : bow ::
   A. composer : instrument.   C. musician : harp.
   B. peg : string.   D. hand : forefinger.

2. The comparison suggests that, like the musician, Odysseus
   A. is nervous before he begins.
   B. works with a stringed instrument.
   C. is proficient in music.
   D. knows his instrument and where to get good strings.

B. Think of a catch that fishermen haul in to a half-moon bay
in a fine-meshed net from the whitecaps of the sea:
how all are poured out on the sand, in throes for the salt sea,
twitching their cold lives away in Helios' fiery air:
so lay the suitors heaped on one another.

1. In the passage, what comparison does Homer use to complete this analogy: *Odysseus :
   suitors* ::
   A. big fish : little fish.   C. Odysseus : enemies.
   B. hunter : catch.   D. fisherman : fish.

2. The comparison suggests that
   A. Odysseus was also a good fisherman.
   B. the suitors had as much chance against Odysseus as fish have when they are caught in
      a net.
   C. something fishy was going on in Ithaca, and Odysseus had to correct it.
   D. the setting of much of the epic is the Greek isles, where fishing is an important industry.

Name _____ Date _____

from the Odyssey, *Part 2* by Homer

Reading: Analyze the Influence of Historical and Cultural Context

The **historical and cultural context** of a work is the backdrop of details of the time and place in which the work is set or in which it was written. These details include the events, beliefs, and customs of a specific culture and time. When you **identify influences on your own reading and responses,** the historical and cultural context reflected in a work becomes more apparent.

- As you read a work from another time and culture, keep your own beliefs and customs in mind.
- Notice the ways in which your reactions to ideas and situations in the work differ from the reactions of the characters.
- Consider whether your reactions reflect your own cultural values.

DIRECTIONS: *For each of the following events or elements in Part 2 of the* Odyssey, *write a few notes on the historical and cultural context. Pay special attention to whether the event or element seems to reflect a universal value or belief or whether it seems specifically rooted in the cultural context of ancient Greece.*

1. Odysseus' reunion with Telemachus

_____

_____

_____

2. the episode focusing on Odysseus' dog, Argus

_____

_____

_____

3. the laziness and arrogance of the suitors

_____

_____

_____

4. Odysseus' and Penelope's testing of each other

_____

_____

_____

5. Odysseus' slaughter of the suitors

_____

_____

_____

from the Odyssey, *Part 2* by Homer
Vocabulary Builder

Word List

dissemble	incredulity	bemusing
equity	maudlin	contempt

A. DIRECTIONS: *In each of the following items, think about the meaning of the italicized word and then answer the question.*

1. From whom would you reasonably expect *equity*—a judge or a thief?

   _____

2. Would you treat someone whom you admire with *contempt*? Why or why not?

   _____

3. Does being *maudlin* involve your intelligence or your emotions? Explain your answer.

   _____

4. Are the intentions of people who *dissemble* likely to be good or bad?

   _____

5. What kind of story or report would inspire *incredulity* in you? Explain.

   _____

6. Would you react to a long, *bemusing* lecture with enthusiasm or with annoyance?

   _____

B. DIRECTIONS: *On the line, write the letter of the choice that is the best synonym for each numbered word.*

____ 1. bemusing
   A. entertaining
   B. reminiscing
   C. stupefying
   D. ingratiating

____ 2. contempt
   A. scorn
   B. petition
   C. agility
   D. cooperation

____ 3. maudlin
   A. transitory
   B. secret
   C. sentimental
   D. mediocre

____ 4. dissemble
   A. arrest
   B. disguise
   C. clarify
   D. reduce

____ 5. equity
   A. justice
   B. medicine
   C. measurement
   D. diagram

____ 6. incredulity
   A. pretension
   B. disbelief
   C. disturbance
   D. hypothesis

from **the Odyssey,** *Part 2* by Homer
Support for Writing a Biography

Use a chart like the one shown to make notes for your biography of Odysseus.

Events That Reveal Odysseus' Character

1. _____
   _____

2. _____
   _____
   _____

3. _____
   _____
   _____

4. _____
   _____
   _____

5. _____
   _____
   _____

Quotations From the Epic

1. _____
   _____

2. _____
   _____

3. _____
   _____

from **the Odyssey, *Part 2*** by Homer
Build Language Skills: Vocabulary

Context Clues

Word roots can provide context clues to help you understand unfamiliar words. The Greek root *techni- (techn)* is used in words related to art, skill, or craft, such as the word *technique*.

> **Example:** Our society depends on *technology* to function.

A. DIRECTIONS: *Use a dictionary, if necessary, to look up the meanings of each of the following words containing the word root* techni-/techn-. *Write one meaning for each word. Then, write a sentence using the word in a context that makes its meaning clear.*

1. technology

   Meaning: _____

   Sentence: _____

2. technocracy

   Meaning: _____

   Sentence: _____

3. technicality

   Meaning: _____

   Sentence: _____

4. technician

   Meaning: _____

   Sentence: _____

Academic Vocabulary Practice

B. DIRECTIONS: *Follow the instructions to write sentences containing the Academic Vocabulary words.*

1. Use *technique* in a sentence about a poet's figurative language.

   _____

2. Use *controversy* in a sentence about an author's biography.

   _____

3. Use *appraise* in a sentence from a drama review.

   _____

4. Use *confirm* in a sentence about an old manuscript.

   _____

5. Use *complex* in a sentence about the plot of a literary work.

   _____

Name _____ Date _____

from **the Odyssey,** *Part 2* by Homer
Build Language Skills: Grammar

Complex and Compound-Complex Sentences

A **complex sentence** consists of one independent clause, which can stand by itself as a sentence, and at least one subordinate clause, which cannot stand by itself as a sentence. A **compound-complex sentence** consists of two or more independent clauses and one or more subordinate clauses.

Complex sentence:	After Odysseus gave Telemachus the signal, Telemachus removed the weapons from the hall.
Compound-complex sentence:	Scholars, who live throughout the world, disagree about whether the epics were composed by the same person, and they also wonder about Homer's historical existence.

A. DIRECTIONS: *Identify each sentence as complex or compound-complex.*

1. Although Odysseus is in disguise, his old dog Argus recognizes him instinctively.

   _____

2. The suitors, who have competed to marry Penelope, behave arrogantly, and they conspire to murder Odysseus' son and heir, Telemachus.

   _____

3. Odysseus becomes anxious when Penelope questions him about the marriage bed.

   _____

4. The *Odyssey*, which has entertained audiences for thousands of years, contains many universal themes; its broad appeal can be explained by Homer's profound understanding of human nature.

   _____

B. Writing Application: *On the following lines, write a paragraph in which you describe a gift that you would like to present to a loved one. In your writing, use all four types of sentences that have been mentioned: simple, compound, complex, and compound-complex. Be prepared to identify each type of sentence.*

_____

_____

_____

_____

_____

_____

_____

_____

Poetry by Edna St. Vincent Millay, Margaret Atwood, Derek Walcott, and Constantine Cavafy
Literary Analysis: Contemporary Interpretations

The characters and events of Homer's *Odyssey* are timeless and universal in their appeal and meaning and have inspired many contemporary interpretations. A **contemporary interpretation** of a literary work is a new piece of writing, such as a poem, story, or play, that a modern-day author bases on an ancient work. An **allusion** is a reference to a well-known person, place, event, literary work, or work of art. By reinventing Homer's tales or by making allusions to them, modern-day writers shed new light on Homer's ancient words. Contemporary interpretations may allude to any aspects of Homer's epic, including plot, characters, settings, imagery and language, and theme.

Even when they are based on the same work, contemporary interpretations can differ widely in purpose and theme. The cultural and historical backgrounds, ideas, attitudes, and beliefs of the contemporary writers profoundly affect their perceptions of the ancient work and the new writings that result.

DIRECTIONS: *Circle the letter of the answer that best completes the sentence.*

1. In Edna St. Vincent Millay's "An Ancient Gesture," the speaker focuses most closely on
   A. Odysseus' travels and the hero's relationships to the gods.
   B. the anguish of Odysseus' son Telemachus.
   C. Penelope's inner grief and frustration at Odysseus' long absence.
   D. the devastation wrought by the Trojan War.

2. In "Siren Song," Margaret Atwood's interpretation of the Sirens suggests that
   A. women are much more complex than they have been given credit for.
   B. the poet herself is not very clever.
   C. men are more clever than they think they are.
   D. women enjoy the roles they play.

3. In "Prologue" and "Epilogue" to the *Odyssey,* Derek Walcott suggests that Billy Blue
   A. has confused the chronological sequence of Odysseus' adventures.
   B. is a modern-day version of Homer, singing the adventures of a "main-man" hero.
   C. believes that we are all capable of behaving as heroically as Odysseus did.
   D. has misinterpreted the character of Penelope.

4. In "Ithaca," Constantine Cavafy sees the wanderings of Odysseus as representing
   A. a grand vacation to exotic places.
   B. the journey through life itself.
   C. a voyage of discovery made possible by such modern conveniences as a credit card.
   D. a trip without a real purpose.

5. In "Ithaca," the lines "Always keep Ithaca fixed in your mind, / . . . But do not hurry the voyage at all" suggest that
   A. the journey is more important than the destination.
   B. we need to know where we are going in life.
   C. everyone should have a home.
   D. some places always remain the same, no matter how other places may change.

Poetry by Edna St. Vincent Millay, Margaret Atwood, Derek Walcott, and Constantine Cavafy

Vocabulary Builder

Word List

authentic	picturesque	siege	lofty	defrauded

A. DIRECTIONS: *Revise each sentence so that the underlined vocabulary word is used logically. Be sure not to change the vocabulary word.*

1. They refused to buy the old silver coin because they believe it is <u>authentic</u>.
   _____

2. Because the landscape was so <u>picturesque</u>, we did not bother to take any photographs.
   _____

3. The <u>siege</u> of the city was successful, so the soldiers outside the walls retreated.
   _____

4. Because he is a person of <u>lofty</u> ideals, we criticize him harshly.
   _____

5. As a merchant with great integrity, he always <u>defrauds</u> his customers.
   _____

B. DIRECTIONS: *On the line, write the letter of the choice that is the best synonym for each numbered word.*

___ 1. defrauded
   A. rejected
   B. praised
   C. cheated
   D. promoted

___ 2. lofty
   A. illusory
   B. pretentious
   C. drafty
   D. noble

___ 3. authentic
   A. genuine
   B. antique
   C. practical
   D. sentimental

___ 4. siege
   A. strong grip
   B. armed blockade
   C. military alliance
   D. crisis intervention

___ 5. picturesque
   A. grotesque
   B. paradoxical
   C. prevalent
   D. charming

Poetry by Edna St. Vincent Millay, Margaret Atwood, Derek Walcott, and Constantine Cavafy

Support for Writing to Compare Literary Works

For each poem in this section, use a chart like the one shown to make prewriting notes for an essay focusing on ways in which Homer's epic poem the *Odyssey* provides worthwhile material for a modern-day writer.

Title of Work: _____   _____
Author's purpose: _____   _____   _____   _____   _____
Contemporary conflict/situation addressed: _____   _____   _____   _____   _____
Additions by contemporary writer: _____   _____   _____   _____   _____
My personal response: _____   _____   _____   _____   _____

Name _____ Date _____

Literary Analysis: Protagonist and Antagonist

The **protagonist** is the chief character in a literary work—the character whose fortunes are of greatest interest to the reader. Some literary works also have an **antagonist**—a character or force that fights the protagonist. The antagonist may be another character or an external force, such as nature, that acts as a character.

Although the protagonist is not always an admirable or even likeable character, readers are interested in what happens to him or her.

- The protagonist's motives may be commonly understood feelings and goals, such as curiosity, the search for love, or the desire to win.
- The protagonist's conflict with the antagonist may represent a larger struggle, such as the conflict between good and evil, success and failure, or life and death.

DIRECTIONS: *Answer the following questions on the lines provided.*

1. Who or what is the protagonist in "Three Skeleton Key"? What is the occupation of the protagonist?

   _____

   _____

2. What qualities or characteristics make the protagonist a bit unusual and attract our interest?

   _____

   _____

   _____

3. Who or what is the antagonist in the story?

   _____

4. How does the author use the technique of personification to make the antagonist seem like a difficult and even dangerous opponent?

   _____

   _____

   _____

5. What parts of the conflict between the protagonist and the antagonist in "Three Skeleton Key" can you identify?

   _____

   _____

Name _____ Date _____

Reading: Compare and Contrast Characters

Comparing and contrasting characters is recognizing and thinking about their similarities and differences. You can compare different characters within a work, characters from different works, or a single character at different points in a particular work. To make a valid, productive comparison, you must examine each character (or the same character at different points in the narrative) in the same way. As you read, ask questions about each character you are comparing in the following general categories. Then, **generate questions after reading** that are specific to the characters and situations in the story.

- What are the character's actions?
- What are the character's reasons for his or her actions?
- What qualities does the character demonstrate?

DIRECTIONS: *Use the space provided to answer these questions about the characters in* "*Three Skeleton Key.*"

1. How does Itchoua contrast with Le Gleo and the narrator?

   _____

2. In the struggle with the rats, how does Le Gleo react differently from the other characters? What does this difference suggest about the ways in which human beings react to extreme pressure or danger?

   _____

   _____

   _____

   _____

3. How successful is Toudouze in personifying the ship's rats, making them seem like characters rather than rats?

   _____

   _____

   _____

4. What attitudes does the narrator display about his profession and Three Skeleton Key at the beginning of the story? What attitudes does he display at the end? What does a comparison of his before-and-after outlooks suggest about the narrator's personality?

   _____

   _____

   _____

   _____

   _____

Name _____ Date _____

Word List

| lurched | diminution | derisive |

A. DIRECTIONS: *Circle the letter of the best answer to each of the following questions.*

1. Which of the following answers is the best synonym for *lurched*?
   A. moved jerkily   B. launched   C. subsided

2. Which of the following answers most nearly means the OPPOSITE of *diminution*?
   A. delay   B. memory   C. increase

3. If you answered someone in a *derisive* fashion, which of the following answers would best describe your tone of voice?
   A. soothing   B. mocking   C. loud

B. DIRECTIONS: *For each of the following items, think about the meaning of the underlined word and then answer the question.*

1. If you wrote a <u>derisive</u> review of a film, would your review be admiring or critical?

   _____

2. If the company for which you worked reported a sharp <u>diminution</u> in sales, would the company's owners feel pleased or concerned?

   _____

3. Would you feel comfortable on a bus that <u>lurched</u> during most of a five-hour journey? Why or why not?

   _____

C. DIRECTIONS: *On the line, write the letter of the answer choice that is the best synonym for each numbered word.*

____ 1. diminution
           A. increase   C. decline
           B. evaluation   D. explanation

____ 2. lurched
           A. staggered   C. climbed
           B. pleaded   D. descended

____ 3. derisive
           A. scoffing   C. smiling
           B. frowning   D. joking

"Three Skeleton Key" by George Toudouze
Support for Writing Journal Entries

For your journal entries, use the following chart to jot down notes.

Timeline: (1) _____
(2) _____
(3) _____
(4) _____
(5) _____
(6) _____
Choice of Days for Journal Entries: (1) _____
(2) _____
(3) _____

As you write, remember to stay in character and make sure that your journal entries reflect any changes that the character experiences in the course of the story.

Name _____ Date _____

Literary Analysis: Protagonist and Antagonist

The **protagonist** is the chief character in a literary work—the character whose fortunes are of greatest interest to the reader. Some literary works also have an **antagonist**—a character or force that fights the protagonist. The antagonist may be another character or an external force, such as nature, that acts as a character.

Although the protagonist is not always an admirable or even likeable character, readers are interested in what happens to him or her.

- The protagonist's motives may be commonly understood feelings and goals, such as curiosity, the search for love, or the desire to win.
- The protagonist's conflict with the antagonist may represent a larger struggle, such as the conflict between good and evil, success and failure, or life and death.

DIRECTIONS: *Answer the following questions on the lines provided.*

1. Who or what is the protagonist in "The Red-headed League"? What is the occupation of the protagonist?

   _____

2. What qualities or characteristics make the protagonist somewhat unusual and attract our interest?

   _____

   _____

   _____

3. Who or what is the antagonist in the story?

   _____

   _____

4. What parts of the conflict between the protagonist and the antagonist in "The Red-headed League" can you identify?

   _____

   _____

   _____

   _____

   _____

   _____

   _____

"The Red-headed League" by Sir Arthur Conan Doyle
Reading: Compare and Contrast Characters

Comparing and contrasting characters is recognizing and thinking about their similarities and differences. You can compare different characters within a work, characters from different works, or a single character at different points in a particular work. To make a valid, productive comparison, you must examine each character (or the same character at different points in the narrative) in the same way. As you read, ask questions about each character you are comparing in the following general categories. Then, **generate questions after reading** that are specific to the characters and situations in the story.

- What are the character's actions?
- What are the character's reasons for his or her actions?
- What qualities does the character demonstrate?

DIRECTIONS: *Use the space provided to answer these questions about the characters in "The Red-headed League."*

1. How does Sherlock Holmes compare and contrast with Dr. Watson?

   _____

   _____

   _____

2. How does Sherlock Holmes contrast with Peter Jones, the police agent from Scotland Yard?

   _____

   _____

   _____

3. How would you compare Sherlock Holmes with his antagonist, the murderer and thief John Clay?

   _____

   _____

   _____

4. How does Holmes's outlook on life at the beginning of "The Red-headed League" compare or contrast with his outlook at the end of the story?

   _____

   _____

   _____

Name _____ Date _____

"The Red-headed League" by Sir Arthur Conan Doyle
Vocabulary Builder

Word List

introspective	vex	formidable

A. DIRECTIONS: *Circle the letter of the best answer to each question.*

1. Which of the following answers is the best synonym for *vex*?
   A. predict   B. annoy   C. promise
2. Which of the following answers most nearly means the OPPOSITE of *introspective*?
   A. outgoing   B. exhausted   C. optimistic
3. Which of the following answers is the best synonym for *formidable*?
   A. bashful   B. lively   C. awe-inspiring

B. DIRECTIONS: *In each of the following items, think about the meaning of the underlined word and then answer the question.*

1. If you faced a <u>formidable</u> enemy, would you face an easy or a difficult challenge?

   _____

2. If you found a situation <u>vexing</u>, would you be pleased or annoyed?

   _____

3. Would a person in an <u>introspective</u> mood be feeling thoughtful, bored, or excited?

   _____

C. DIRECTIONS: *On the line, write the letter of the answer choice that is the best synonym for each numbered word.*

____ 1. introspective
     A. occupied   C. thoughtful
     B. sneaky   D. careful

____ 2. vex
     A. promote   C. irritate
     B. decorate   D. settle

____ 3. formidable
     A. impolite   C. friendly
     B. frightening   D. impressive

"The Red-headed League" by Sir Arthur Conan Doyle
Support for Writing Journal Entries

For your journal entries, use the following chart to jot down notes.

Timeline: (1) _____

(2) _____

(3) _____

(4) _____

(5) _____

(6) _____

Choice of Days for Journal Entries: (1) _____

(2) _____

(3) _____

As you write, remember to stay in character and make sure that your journal entries reflect any changes that the character experiences in the course of the story.

"Three Skeleton Key" by George Toudouze
"The Red-headed League" by Sir Arthur Conan Doyle
Build Language Skills: Vocabulary

The Word Root -sign-

The Latin word root -sign- means "sign," as in the English words "signal" or "significance."

A. DIRECTIONS: *Use a dictionary, if necessary, to look up the meanings of each of the following words containing the word root -sign-. Write one meaning for each word. Then, write a sentence using the word in a context that makes its meaning clear.*

1. signature

   Meaning: _____

   Sentence: _____

2. insignificant

   Meaning: _____

   Sentence: _____

3. signify

   Meaning: _____

   Sentence: _____

4. consignee

   Meaning: _____

   Sentence: _____

Academic Vocabulary Practice

B. DIRECTIONS: *Answer each question using the underlined Academic Vocabulary word.*

1. If an argument is <u>cogent</u>, would you find it persuasive or flimsy?

   _____

2. Would a good detective pay attention to the <u>significant</u> details of a case? Why or why not?

   _____

3. If you spotted a <u>defect</u> in one of your essays, would you try to correct it? Why or why not?

   _____

4. Would a <u>compelling</u> public speaker be likely to sway the opinions of his or her audience?

   _____

5. In a <u>coherent</u> essay, does the writer present ideas out of order or in an organized way?

   _____

Name _____ Date _____

"Three Skeleton Key" by George Toudouze
"The Red-headed League" by Sir Arthur Conan Doyle
Build Language Skills: Grammar

Using Commas Correctly

Study the following list, which contains helpful suggestions on correct comma usage.

- Use a comma before the coordinating conjunction to separate two independent clauses in a compound sentence.

  We wanted to attend the concert, but our friends wanted to stay home.

- Use commas to separate three or more words, phrases, or clauses in a series.

  She bought onions, tomatoes, and peas.

- Use a comma after an introductory word, phrase, or clause.

  At the end of our day at the beach, we returned home.

- Use commas to set off parenthetical and nonessential expressions.

  His painting, which I saw yesterday, is difficult to understand.

- Use commas with places, dates, and titles.

  Edgar Allan Poe was raised in Richmond, Virginia.

- Use a comma to set off a direct quotation.

  Teresa asked, "Has everyone had enough salad?"

A. DIRECTIONS: *Rewrite the following sentences, adding commas where they are needed.*

1. Sir Arthur Conan Doyle the creator of Sherlock Holmes first studied to be an eye doctor.

   _____

2. When Doyle was in medical school he became aware of a certain professor.

   _____

3. This doctor who could diagnose illnesses that puzzled his colleagues may have been the model for the great Sherlock Holmes.

   _____

B. Writing Application: *On the following lines, write a paragraph in which you tell what you like or dislike about detective stories. Use a variety of sentence structures, and be sure you use commas correctly.*

_____

_____

_____

_____

"There Is a Longing" by Chief Dan George
Literary Analysis: Author's Philosophical Assumptions

An author's **purpose,** or goal, is shaped by his or her **philosophical assumptions,** or basic beliefs. These philosophical assumptions may be political, moral, or ethical beliefs. They may be assumptions about human nature. The author may use basic beliefs as support for an argument. The response of the **audience,** or readers, to the author's work will depend on whether the audience shares the author's beliefs.

To read with understanding, find the basic beliefs and assumptions in the author's work. Decide whether you accept them and whether others would be likely to accept them. Then, evaluate whether these assumptions support the author's purpose.

DIRECTIONS: *Consider the philosophical assumption, or basic belief, underlying each of the following passages from "There Is a Longing." Then, write a brief note on the chart to identify and comment on the philosophical assumption.*

Passage	Philosophical Assumption
1. There is a longing in the heart of my people to reach out and grasp that which is needed for our survival.	
2. But they will emerge with their hand held forward, not to receive welfare, but to grasp the place in society that is rightly ours.	
3. Oh, Great Spirit! Give me back the courage of the olden Chiefs. Let me wrestle with my surroundings. Let me once again, live in harmony with my environment.	
4. Like the thunderbird of old, I shall rise again out of the sea; I shall grab the instruments of the white man's success—his education, his skills.	
5. I shall see our young braves and our chiefs sitting in the houses of law and government, ruling and being ruled by the knowledge and freedoms of our great land.	

Name _____ Date _____

Reading: Recognize Compare-and-Contrast Organization

Comparing and contrasting means recognizing similarities and differences. In persuasive writing, authors often compare and contrast one point of view with another. As you read, use **self-monitoring** techniques like the ones shown to make sure you understand the comparisons.

- Find the things or ideas being compared.
- Restate the similarities and differences in your own words.
- Explain the significance of the similarities and differences.

If you cannot find, restate, or explain the author's points, reread words or phrases that were unclear, and make sure you understand them.

DIRECTIONS: *Answer the following questions to self-monitor your reading of "There Is a Longing."*

1. According to Chief Dan George, how would the "new warriors" contrast with those of "olden days"?

_____

_____

_____

2. Once the "new warriors" accepted and mastered the challenge, how would Native American society of the future contrast with the conditions that existed in Chief Dan George's time?

_____

_____

_____

3. How does Chief Dan George say that he differed from past chiefs?

_____

_____

4. In what ways does the chief hope that he might be like past chiefs?

_____

_____

Name _____ Date _____

Word List

---
determination   endurance

A. DIRECTIONS: *Circle the letter of the best answer to each of the following questions.*

1. Which of the following is the best synonym for *determination*?
   A. accuracy   B. firm intention   C. sudden decision
2. Which of the following most nearly means the OPPOSITE of *endurance*?
   A. energy   B. complaint   C. weakness

B. DIRECTIONS: *In each of the following items, think about the meaning of the underlined word and then answer the question.*

1. Would running 26 miles require <u>endurance</u>? Why or why not?

   _____

2. If you faced a challenge or task with <u>determination</u>, would your mind be made up to master or complete it? Explain.

   _____

C. DIRECTIONS: *On the line, write the letter of the choice that is the best synonym for each numbered word.*

____ 1. determination
   A. warmth   C. firmness
   B. accuracy   D. speed

____ 2. endurance
   A. cruelty   C. sympathy
   B. style   D. strength

Name _____ Date _____

Use the following chart to make prewriting notes for your letter to Chief Dan George about his speech.

Words That Show Your Reactions
_____
_____
Support in "There Is a Longing" for Your Reactions
_____
_____
Reason(s) for Writing Your Letter
_____
_____
What People Can Learn From the Message in "There Is a Longing"
_____
_____

On a separate page, write a letter using your notes. Make sure that you maintain a respectful tone.

Name _____ Date _____

"Glory and Hope" by Nelson Mandela
Literary Analysis: Author's Philosophical Assumptions

An author's **purpose,** or goal, is shaped by his or her **philosophical assumptions,** or basic beliefs. These philosophical assumptions may be political, moral, or ethical beliefs. They may be assumptions about human nature. The author may use basic beliefs as support for an argument. The response of the **audience,** or readers, to the author's work will depend on whether the audience shares the author's beliefs.

To read with understanding, find the basic beliefs and assumptions in the author's work. Decide whether you accept them and whether others would be likely to accept them. Then, evaluate whether these assumptions support the author's purpose.

DIRECTIONS: *Consider the philosophical assumption, or basic belief, underlying each of the following passages from "Glory and Hope." Then, write a brief note on the chart to identify and comment on the philosophical assumption.*

Passage	Philosophical Assumption
1. Out of an experience of an extraordinary human disaster that lasted too long must be born a society of which all humanity will be proud.	
2. Each time one of us touches the soil of this land, we feel a sense of personal renewal.	

3. The time for the healing of the wounds has come.
   The moment to bridge the chasms that divide us has come.
   The time to build is upon us.	

4. We enter into a covenant that we shall build a society in which all South Africans, both black and white, will be able to walk tall, without any fear in their hearts, assured of their inalienable right to human dignity—a rainbow nation at peace with itself and the world.	
5. Never, never, and never again shall it be that this beautiful land will again experience the oppression of one by another. . . .	

Name _____ Date _____

"Glory and Hope" by Nelson Mandela
Reading: Recognize Compare-and-Contrast Organization

Comparing and contrasting means recognizing similarities and differences. In persuasive writing, authors often compare and contrast one point of view with another. As you read, use **self-monitoring** techniques like the ones shown to make sure you understand the comparisons.

- Find the things or ideas being compared.
- Restate the similarities and differences in your own words.
- Explain the significance of the similarities and differences.

If you cannot find, restate, or explain the author's points, reread words or phrases that were unclear and make sure you understand them.

DIRECTIONS: *Answer the following questions to self-monitor your reading of "Glory and Hope."*

1. According to Nelson Mandela, how does the present in South Africa contrast with the past?
   _____
   _____
   _____

2. How does South Africa's international standing now contrast with its position in the past?
   _____
   _____
   _____

3. How does Nelson Mandela's portrait of a future society in South Africa strengthen the contrasts he has drawn between the present and the past?
   _____
   _____
   _____
   _____

Name _____ Date _____

"Glory and Hope" by Nelson Mandela
Vocabulary Builder

Word List

confer	pernicious	covenant

A. DIRECTIONS: *Circle the letter of the best answer to each question.*

1. Which of the following is the best synonym for *confer*?
   A. divide   B. respect   C. give

2. Which of the following most nearly means the OPPOSITE of *pernicious*?
   A. negative   B. harmless   C. courageous

3. If you have made a *covenant* with someone, what did you probably exchange?
   A. information   B. directions   C. solemn promises

B. DIRECTIONS: *For each item, think about the meaning of the underlined word and then answer the question.*

1. Would a <u>covenant</u> typically involve an advertisement or a promise? Explain.

   _____

2. If you regarded a person as <u>pernicious</u>, would you recommend him or her for a job? Explain.

   _____

3. If you <u>confer</u> an award on someone, do you give it or do you take it away?

   _____

C. DIRECTIONS: *On the line, write the letter of the choice that is the best synonym for each numbered word.*

____ 1. pernicious
    A. childlike   C. damaging
    B. early   D. enhancing

____ 2. confer
    A. give   C. magnify
    B. support   D. reproach

____ 3. covenant
    A. conceal   C. protest
    B. agreement   D. invitation

"Glory and Hope" by Nelson Mandela
Support for Writing a Letter

Use the following chart to make prewriting notes for your letter to Nelson Mandela about his speech.

Words That Show Your Reactions
_____
_____
Support in "Glory and Hope" for Your Reactions
_____
_____
Reason(s) for Writing Your Letter
_____
What People Can Learn From the Message in "Glory and Hope"
_____
_____

On a separate page, write a letter using your notes. Make sure that you maintain a respectful tone.

"There Is a Longing" by Chief Dan George
"Glory and Hope" by Nelson Mandela
Build Language Skills: Vocabulary

The Word Root -her-

The Latin word root -her- means "to cling or stick together." An argument that is *coherent* "clings together": It is well organized and convincing. Sometimes, this root appears as -hes-, as in the word *adhesive*, which means "sticking" or "clinging to."

A. DIRECTIONS: *Use a dictionary, if necessary, to look up the meanings of each of the following words containing the word root -her- or -hes-. Write one meaning for each word. Then, write a sentence using the word in a context that makes its meaning clear.*

1. inherent

   Meaning: _____

   Sentence: _____

2. adherent

   Meaning: _____

   Sentence: _____

3. cohesive

   Meaning: _____

   Sentence: _____

4. hesitation

   Meaning: _____

   Sentence: _____

Academic Vocabulary Practice

B. DIRECTIONS: *Follow the instructions to write sentences containing the underlined Academic Vocabulary words.*

1. Use <u>cogent</u> in a sentence about an argument to give the vote to teenagers.

   _____

2. Use <u>significant</u> in a sentence about a recent story in the news.

   _____

3. Use <u>defect</u> in a sentence about a machine that does not work properly.

   _____

4. Use <u>compelling</u> in a sentence about a commercial you have seen on television.

   _____

5. Use <u>coherent</u> in a sentence about an explanation you have read.

   _____

Name _____ Date _____

"There Is a Longing" by Chief Dan George

"Glory and Hope" by Nelson Mandela

Build Language Skills: Grammar

Using Colons, Semicolons, and Ellipsis Points Correctly

Use a **colon** in order to introduce a list of items following an independent clause, to introduce a formal quotation, or to follow the salutation in a business letter.

- He bought materials for the salad: lettuce, tomatoes, onions, and radishes.
- Nelson Mandela evokes his fellow South Africans' love for their land in these words: "Each time one of us touches the soil of this land, we feel a sense of personal renewal."
- Dear Sir:

Use a **semicolon** to join independent clauses that are not already joined by a conjunction. Also, use a semicolon to avoid confusion when independent clauses or items in a series already contain commas.

- The government of South Africa finally rejected apartheid; in 1994, the first free elections were held.
- We visited Boston, Philadelphia, and Washington, D.C.; altogether, our tour of the eastern seaboard was a great success.

Ellipsis points (. . .) are punctuation marks that are used to show that something has not been expressed. Usually, ellipsis points indicate one of the following situations:

- Words have been left out of a quotation.
- A series continues beyond the items mentioned.
- Time passes or action occurs in a narrative.

- Nelson Mandela says, "We are moved . . . when the grass turns green and the flowers bloom."
- We thought wistfully about the cats' curiosity, agility, and grace. . . .
- They keep their discontent to themselves . . . but will they do so forever?

A. DIRECTIONS: *Rewrite each sentence on the lines provided, correcting errors in the use of colons, semicolons, and ellipsis points. There is only one error in each sentence.*

1. Julius Caesar described his victory as follows . . . "I came, I saw, I conquered."

   _____

2. Statesmanship is a rare gift, few heads of government in the modern world, in fact, have risen to its challenges.

   _____

   _____

B. Writing Application: *On the lines, write a paragraph in which you describe a favorite animal or bird. In your paragraph, use at least one example of each of the following: a colon, a semicolon, and ellipsis points.*

_____

_____

_____

_____

Unit 6 Resources: Themes in Literature

Name _____ Date _____

Literary Analysis: Tall Tale and Myth

A **tall tale** is a type of folk tale that contains some or all of the following features:

- a larger-than-life central hero
- far-fetched situations and amazing feats
- humor
- *hyperbole*, or exaggeration

Tall tales are a particularly American form of story. Many tall tales originated during the American frontier period and reflect the challenges and values of that place and time.

A **myth** is an anonymous story that explains the actions of gods or human heroes, the reasons for certain traditions, or the causes of natural features. Every culture has its own *mythology*, or collection of myths, which express the central values of the people who created them. **Mythic heroes** often share three characteristics: they have at least one divine parent, they gain special knowledge or weapons, and they face seemingly impossible tasks. In general, myths tell how gods shape human life while tall tales tell how humans make things happen.

DIRECTIONS: *Write your answers to the following questions on the lines provided.*

1. How would you compare and contrast Pecos Bill and Perseus as **heroes?**

   _____

   _____

2. What elements of **exaggeration** or **fantasy** can you identify in each tale?

   "Pecos Bill: The Cyclone": _____

   _____

   "Perseus": _____

   _____

3. **Mood** is the overall atmosphere or feeling created by a literary work. **Tone** is the author's attitude toward the subject, the characters, or the audience. How would you compare and contrast "Pecos Bill: The Cyclone" with "Perseus" in mood and tone?

   Mood: _____

   _____

   Tone: _____

   _____

4. In their original versions, many tall tales and myths were **oral literature**—or works that were passed down by word of mouth from one generation to the next. What qualities in "The Cyclone" and "Perseus" would lend themselves especially well to oral storytelling?

   _____

   _____

"Pecos Bill: The Cyclone" by Harold W. Felton and
"Perseus" by Edith Hamilton
Vocabulary Builder

Word List

usurped	skeptics	mortified	revelry

A. DIRECTIONS: *Revise each sentence so that the underlined vocabulary word is used logically. Be sure not to change the vocabulary word.*

1. After the tyrant <u>usurped</u> the king's throne, most people acclaimed him as the legitimate ruler.

   _____

2. The professor's arguments were so convincing that many <u>skeptics</u> questioned her conclusions.

   _____

3. When Eugene made such diplomatic comments to our hosts, we felt <u>mortified</u>.

   _____

4. The sounds of <u>revelry</u> from the party next door were low and soothing.

   _____

B. DIRECTIONS: *On the line, write the letter of the choice that is the best synonym for each numbered word.*

___ 1. revelry
   A. slow improvement
   B. agile maneuver
   C. early departure
   D. noisy merrymaking

___ 2. usurped
   A. researched
   B. incorporated
   C. seized power
   D. reorganized

___ 3. skeptics
   A. allies
   B. doubters
   C. forecasters
   D. inventors

___ 4. mortified
   A. buried
   B. embarrassed
   C. disguised
   D. deceived

Name _____ Date _____

"Pecos Bill: The Cyclone" by Harold W. Felton and
"Perseus" by Edith Hamilton

Support for Writing to Compare Literary Works

Use a chart like the one shown to make prewriting notes for an essay comparing and
contrasting the values that Pecos Bill and Perseus represent.

Values	Pecos Bill	Perseus
Respect		
Fears		
Goals		
Achievements		
Motivations